Relaxing
Mindfulness
Puzzles

De-stress with this calming collection

ARCTURUS

ARCTURUS

This edition published in 2019 by Arcturus Publishing Limited
26/27 Bickels Yard, 151–153 Bermondsey Street,
London SE1 3HA

ISBN: 978-1-78950-381-4
AD007077NT

Printed in the UK

CONTENTS

Introduction

"Take care of this moment."

Gandhi

Mindfulness asks little from us, only that we take care of this moment. It's surprising how hard that can be.

In a world that is angry and fractured, where the news feed on our phones brings even more reasons for anger, this moment easily becomes a place where we feel trapped.

That trap, though, is our own. Marcus Aurelius explained this best: "You have power over your mind—not outside events. Realize this, and you will find strength."

So take a moment for yourself. Focus on here, focus on now. Yesterday is behind you, tomorrow will unfold at its own pace. Let mindfulness bring you back to today. To this moment, now.

That's all mindfulness means. And it's a practice that can be easily developed. There's no need for yoga classes or learning to meditate. You can simply solve a puzzle.

A puzzle is a problem with a solution, one that you will certainly find. Every puzzle in this book has easy-to-follow instructions and all the information you need to make an attempt.

The puzzles are of various types. Some you may recognize; others may be unfamiliar. You may find yourself trying one approach, then realizing it doesn't work and reaching for another. The point is, the puzzle is here and now—and so are you.

Don't let yourself believe this is a waste of your time. Self-indulgent even. Mindfulness is not self-indulgent. Mindfulness is looking after yourself. Studies have shown that the ability to

focus on the present, and on what you can do, enhances well-being and reduces stress. In turn, this boosts creativity and undermines self-doubt.

It is when we leave self-doubt behind that we are able to see the truth of another insight from Marcus Aurelius: "Everything we hear is an opinion, not a fact. Everything we see is a perspective, not the truth."

Remember that, and it's easier to reject anger and to discover what it is you really think.

We hope that these puzzles help you relax, show you how to cultivate mindfulness—and lead the way back to yourself.

"Sometimes the most important thing in a whole day is the rest we take between two deep breaths."

Etty Hillesum

1   Maze

Start at the top and find a path to the middle of the maze.

"Silence is the great teacher,
and to learn its lessons you
must pay attention to it. There
is no substitute for the creative
inspiration, knowledge, and stability
that come from knowing how to
contact your core of inner silence."

Deepak Chopra

 6

2   Wordsearch: Islands of the Pacific

Can you find all of the listed words hidden in the grid below?
Words run horizontally, vertically or diagonally, in either a forward or
backward direction.

```
P A P K A O P A P A T B W D E
U U C L J J S C N P E N U M G
I H V L H N A W I A T C I A I
T K S E V L A L L G I D O L G
A P E N R H Y N A E S R E D F
M V A N O T B P H U A E D E R
I S R E J H A E K I H A M N Q
T A I R U A S S A N E C K E R
I H R L A B O T S I R C N A S
R O E V L K E I S R I A U Z I
I W T J X A O F A R I P N H V
K L S C N H W T H A W A I I R
X A A W E N C A S W S N V G A
B N E W C A L E D O N I A H J
B D S M U R U R O A V U K G W
```

DUCIE	KIRITIMATI	PENRHYN
EASTER	MAHIKEA	RAIATEA
FLINT	MALDEN	RENNELL
HAWAII	MURUROA	SAKHALIN
HONSHU	NASSAU	SAN
HOWLAND	NECKER	CRISTOBAL
JARVIS	NEW	TAIWAN
KAOPAPA	CALEDONIA	VOSTOK
	NUNIVAK	WALLIS

Arroword

Solve the clues, then enter each answer in the direction of the arrows, one letter per square.

Billiards stick	▼	Type of Italian brandy	▼	Wounding or wittily pointed remarks	Round-about way	▼	Condiment, sodium chloride	Plot of ground in which plants grow
African country ►		▼			▼		Snakelike	▼
►				Additional ►			▼	
German form of address for a man	Bordered against ►	▼						
►				Card game, a form of rummy		Food wrapped in a pastry shell		Put in
Mountain range	Certain		Informal term for a drink of tea ►	▼		▼		▼
Having a regular wage	▼ ►							
Necktie		Inspires wonder in	Air-hole		Come to a halt ►			
◣		▼	▼			Rend		Implore
Female sheep ►					Chest bone ►	▼		▼
Prospect	Interlace ►							
◣					Pin ►			

4   Sudoku

Place one of the numbers from 1 to 9 into every empty cell so that each row, each column and each 3x3 block contains all the numbers from 1 to 9.

9			6		3			2
		5				8		1
	4	7		2	1			6
				1	4	6	8	
	3		5		6		9	
	6	2	3	7				
2			7	9		3	4	
4		8				7		
5			4		8			9

 "Don't let yesterday use up too much of today."

Cherokee proverb

5   Codeword

Every letter in this puzzle has been replaced by a number, the number remaining the same for that letter wherever it occurs. Every letter of the alphabet has been used. Substitute numbers for letters to complete the codeword.

It may help to cross off the letters beneath the grid to keep a track of progress, and to use the reference box showing which numbers have been decoded. Three letters have already been entered into the grid, to help you on your way.

3	24	10	9	24	10	10	■	■	5	7	23	1	1	23
21		22		3		6	24	21	7		4			3
6	21	23	16	21		7			24		11			21
4		6		8	11	19	9		8	23	20	12	24	8
23	6 **L**	21	19	4		20	21	6	4			21		11
	11 **O**			24			8		21			14		24
23	4 **T**	4	24	22		17	7	10	4	24	2	24	21	3
10		23		23		23		24		8		8		23
10	7	8	2	6	11	18	21	19		16	24	1	24	6
21		12		7		23			24			8		
10		21		4	21	10	4		10	9	11	12	21	
10	13	19	24	9	20		14	21	4	24		15		16
24			3		11			20		25	23	24	26	21
8			11		10	23	9	21		6		3		19
1	24	9	6	21	4	■	■	21	6	21	9	21	8	4

A B C D E F G H I J K L M
N O P Q R S T U V W X Y Z

1	2	3	4 **T**	5	6 **L**	7	8	9	10	11 **O**	12	13
14	15	16	17	18	19	20	21	22	23	24	25	26

6   **Domino Placement**

A standard set of 28 dominoes has been laid out as shown. Can you draw in the edges of them all?

The check-box is provided as an aid, so that you can see which dominoes have been located.

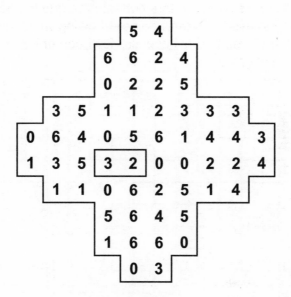

0-0	0-1	0-2	0-3	0-4	0-5	0-6	1-1	1-2	1-3	1-4	1-5	1-6	2-2

2-3	2-4	2-5	2-6	3-3	3-4	3-5	3-6	4-4	4-5	4-6	5-5	5-6	6-6
✓													

"Forever is composed of nows."

Emily Dickinson

7   Criss Cross: "SNOW..."

The words are provided, but can you fit them all into the grid?

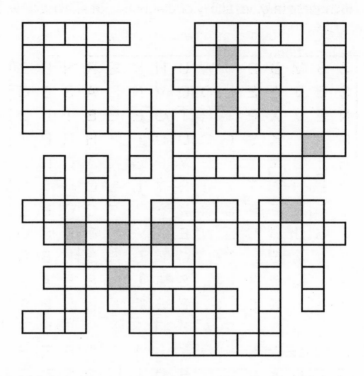

3 letters	5 letters	6 letters
CAT	BLIND	BOARDS
MEN	BOOTS	CANNON
	BOUND	CAPPED
4 letters	FENCE	FLURRY
BELT	FIELD	MOBILE
CONE	GLOBE	ORCHID
DROP	GOOSE	
FALL	SCAPE	**7 letters**
LINE	SHOES	COVERED
MELT	SLIDE	LEOPARD
SUIT	STORM	MACHINE
	UNDER	

8 Wordsearch: A Walk in the Woods

Can you find all of the listed words hidden in the grid below? Words run horizontally, vertically or diagonally, in either a forward or backward direction.

```
Z B M B B U W U H V E R N H G
S E V A E L O Q V N E A B B G
N E V X P I R T O E E B I E D
D A L K S L C D D F A H R R H
E Z D T T X E Y P O N A C R E
A L H W T Y J B Y L L O H I M
L E I F R E R X B I Y Q C E L
P G J H U A N E W A E M E S O
S V Z S N B L O N G S U E B C
I I Q C K T L S A E W S B A K
X A H K E L T E S O E H H D W
S E U E I R A S C S S R D G T
S W B W E P O Y S I E O G E R
C F F A V M U S D L C O G R A
X O M S H T A P R A S M K C Q
```

BADGER	DEER	MOSSES
BEECH	FOLIAGE	MUSHROOM
BEETLE	GREENERY	NETTLES
BERRIES	HEMLOCK	PATHS
BIRCH	HOLLY	STREAM
BRANCHES	LEAVES	TRUNK
CANOPY	LICHEN	TWIGS
CROW	MAPLE	WILLOW

9   Number Link

Working from one square to another, horizontally or vertically (never diagonally), draw single continuous paths to pair up each set of two matching numbers.

No line may cross another, none may travel through any square containing a number, and every square must be visited just once.

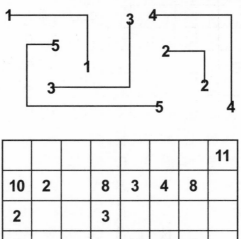

							11
10	2		8	3	4	8	
2			3				
6				10	9	4	
7		5					
				1			7
	6	5		9	1	11	

"Do not encumber your mind with useless thoughts. What good does it do to brood on the past or anticipate the future? Remain in the simplicity of the present moment."

Dilgo Khyentse Rinpoche

10 Pyragram

Every clue in this puzzle is an anagram leading to a single-word solution. Correctly solve the anagram on each level of the pyramid and another word will appear, reading down the central column.

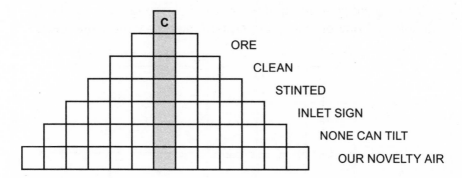

ORE

CLEAN

STINTED

INLET SIGN

NONE CAN TILT

OUR NOVELTY AIR

11 Word Wheel

How many words of three or more letters can you make from those in the wheel, without using plurals, abbreviations or proper nouns?

The central letter must appear once in every word and no letter in a section of the wheel may be used more than once.

There is at least one nine-letter word in the wheel.

Nine-letter word(s):

_____

12   Arroword

Solve the clues, then enter each answer in the direction of the arrows, one letter per square.

Make peace, come to terms ▼		Famous person (abbr) ▼		Takes part in a fist fight	Bird of New Zealand ▼		Incline ▼
⌐							
Period of economic decline		Heavy open wagon		Immoral act ▼	Blackthorn fruit ▼		Drama set to music ▼
⌐		▼					
Aromatic herb ►					Distur-bance, usually in protest ▼		Senior woman in a pro-fession or class ▼
Club	Become less intense ▼		Made a written record of ►				
⌐			Consumed	Basic unit of currency in Germany ►			
Chris-tening		Closely confined ▼		Mosque official ▼	Beam of light ►		
⌐						Very small	
Move in large numbers ►				Be in posses-sion of ►		▼	
►			Exotic ►				
Hideout	Male cat ►			Bruce ___, expert kung fu actor ►			

Sudoku

Place one of the numbers from 1 to 9 into every empty cell so that each row, each column and each 3x3 block contains all the numbers from 1 to 9.

8	7		5			3		
	9	4		6	7	5		
	6		2					9
	5			2		1		6
2			7		5			4
9		7		4			3	
7					1		8	
		3	6	8		9	1	
		1			9		5	2

"Every moment and every event of every man's life on earth plants something in his soul."

Thomas Merton

14   Codeword

Every letter in this puzzle has been replaced by a number, the number remaining the same for that letter wherever it occurs. Every letter of the alphabet has been used. Substitute numbers for letters to complete the codeword.

It may help to cross off the letters beneath the grid to keep a track of progress, and to use the reference box showing which numbers have been decoded. Three letters have already been entered into the grid, to help you on your way.

8	█	15	█	24	26	5	8	17	8	26	5	8	26	16
20	8	26	11	26	█	3	█	█	10	█	25	█	15	█
16	█	23	█	24	26	16	8	19	9	19	8	8	5	2
19	11	11	2	16	█	8	█	█	8	█	13	█	21	█
11	█	26	█	24	█	5	19	24	14	14	13	24	8	19
7	█	1	15	3	6	█	24	█	14	█	█	26	█	8
8	10	15	█	16	█	█	2	█	13	█	9	8	3	15
19	█	8	█	8	26	22	11	6	8	5	█	20	█	17
16	15	19	4	█	3	█	16	█	█	8	█	3	2	12
8	█	8	█	2	█	16	█	8	17	24	23	█	█	11
5	8	5	15	23	16	24 I	11 O	26 N	█	11	█	16	█	13
█	7	█	13	█	24	█	█	6	█	19	15	26	21	2
23	11	15	26	16	8	19	17	13	11	16	█	8	█	16
█	18	█	3	█	2	█	█	11	█	8	26	2	15	8
16	8	3	19	2	16	3	24	26	8	5	█	2	█	19

A B C D E F G H I J K L M

N O P Q R S T U V W X Y Z

1	2	3	4	5	6	7	8	9	10	11	12	13
										O		

14	15	16	17	18	19	20	21	22	23	24	25	26
										I		N

Wordsearch: Writing

Can you find all of the listed words hidden in the grid below?
Words run horizontally, vertically or diagonally, in either a forward or
backward direction.

```
C L A N O I T A M R I F N O C
N E R I M T P I E C E R N P N
I T A L I C S H S D A M D E E
G N I D A E R S O M E M T N T
I N V O I C E R E T L B P E T
G O A C Y R F D I F O E I R I
R L U J D U E N R S H C T S R
A O H D T N R A E A R N O A W
M C A B S D E H T P C A S P Q
M I N U T E N T L E T T E R Y
A M L V E R C R A M A P S D T
R E Y E Y L E O P M I E A O O
H S S G E I G H P E N C I L P
M A I L I N G S A T I C E N A
D E L Y R E V I L E D A R M S
```

ACCEPTANCE	LETTER	READING
ADDRESS	MAILING	RECEIPT
CONFIRMATION	MEMOS	REFERENCE
DEAR SIR	MINUTE	SEMICOLON
DELIVERY	OPENER	SHORTHAND
GRAMMAR	PENCIL	STAMPS
INVOICE	PHOTOCOPY	UNDERLINE
ITALICS	POSTCARD	WRITTEN

16   Criss Cross: On Vacation

The words are provided, but can you fit them all into the grid?

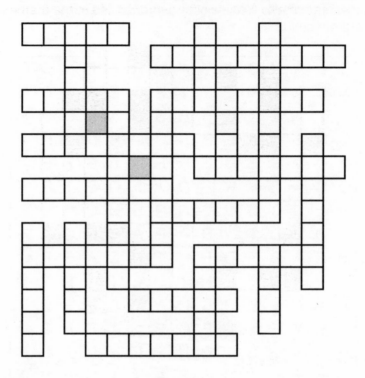

4 letters	6 letters	8 letters
AWAY	BIKINI	PASSPORT
MAPS	CAMERA	POSTCARD
TAXI	OUTING	SUITCASE
	VOYAGE	

5 letters		9 letters
CABIN	7 letters	APARTMENT
GROUP	AIRPORT	EMBARKING
GUIDE	DAY TRIP	EXCURSION
HOTEL	JOURNEY	
VIEWS	TOURIST	
	VISITOR	

Flower Power

Fit the listed words into the grid below, then rearrange the letters in the shaded squares to form another word related to the theme of this book.

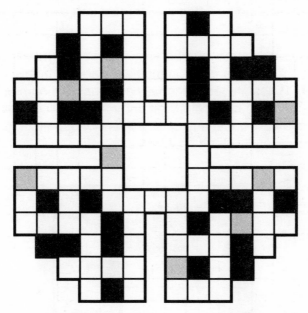

3 letters	4 letters		5 letters	
BET	AKIN	ETCH	CHESS	SABLE
CAB	BIKE	HALO	ETHOS	TARDY
DAM	BLOT	LANE	GLASS	TATTY
EGG	BOOM	RIND	LIGHT	TEASE
ELK	BUNK	SCUD	NORSE	TYING
OPT	DENY	WAFT	OOZED	WAGON
YET				
ZOO				

"A man is but the product
of his thoughts; what he
thinks, he becomes."

Mahatma Gandhi

18   Light Up

Place circles (representing light bulbs) in some of the empty squares, in such a way that no two bulbs shine on each other, until every square of the grid is lit up. A bulb sends rays of light horizontally and vertically, illuminating its entire row and column unless its light is blocked by a black cell.

Some black cells contain numbers, indicating how many light bulbs are in adjacent squares either immediately above, below, to the right, or to the left. Bulbs placed diagonally adjacent to a numbered cell do not contribute to the bulb count. An unnumbered black cell may have any number of light bulbs adjacent to it, or none at all, and not all light bulbs are necessarily clued via black squares.

(grid puzzle)

> "I have found my greatest
> moments of joy and
> peace just sitting in
> silence, and then I take
> that joy and peace with
> me out into the world."

Holly Mosier

19   Sudoku

Place one of the numbers from 1 to 9 into every empty cell so that each row, each column and each 3x3 block contains all the numbers from 1 to 9.

			5	2	9	6		
4	9	6		3		7		
			7		4	1		
5			3		1		6	
	3	8				4	2	
	6		4		2			1
		3	8		5			
		7		1		5	9	8
		5	9	7	6			

"Everything is based on mind,
is led by mind, is fashioned
by mind. If you speak
and act with a pure mind,
happiness will follow you, as
a shadow clings to a form."

Buddha

20   Arroword

Solve the clues, then enter each answer in the direction of the arrows, one letter per square.

Inferior in strength or significance	Abreast of	Immense cloud of gas and dust in space	▼	Text of a song	Group of people attractively arranged	Deadbeat	▼	Joint protected in front by the patella
				Fork prong ►				
Spread or diffuse through ►								Court
Judo belt ►				Exhaled with force ►				
							Unit of gravitational force	
Finger joint	High and tight collar		Whitish 'meal' drunk before an x-ray	Consequently ►				
				Decree that prohibits something		No longer new, uninteresting		Adjust again after an initial failure
Blackleg		Maltreater ►						
					Beat hard		Came first	
Venomous hooded snake	Relatives by marriage (2-4)							
				Succulent plant ►				
Bill of fare		Instant ►						

21   Wordsearch: World Heritage Sites

Can you find all of the listed words hidden in the grid below?
Words run horizontally, vertically or diagonally, in either a forward or
backward direction.

```
A N J A R O E T E M O I I O X
D N T I M G E D B L A Y L E S
A D L I K T S Z D R U D A G D
S Y B A D F E R M W T P N E A
A L D A B R A A T O L L J L L
M S A B G U R N W F M U S K A
P T E G M I U N E R A V A P K
A D A A E O O L I D O S T E N
P U A S M F S O L E D S A T A
H A U G C N E A O L S N I R H
O Q Q O M E Y R M C E L H A C
S O R I Z I R F Y M N G T U T
Y F E A Y I T W U T F R Y I I
U X N I Y A N B C H A V I N A
O F A L I X A T A J M A H A L
```

ABU MENA	MASADA	ST KILDA
AKSUM	METEORA	TAJ MAHAL
ALDABRA ATOLL	MOUNT WUYI	TAXILA
ANJAR	OLD RAUMA	TIMGAD
CHAVIN	OLD TOWN OF CORFU	TIYA
DELOS	PAPHOS	TSODILO
HATRA	PETRA	TYRE
ITCHAN KALA	QUSEIR AMRA	YIN XU

Codeword

Every letter in this puzzle has been replaced by a number, the number remaining the same for that letter wherever it occurs. Every letter of the alphabet has been used. Substitute numbers for letters to complete the codeword.

It may help to cross off the letters beneath the grid to keep a track of progress, and to use the reference box showing which numbers have been decoded. Three letters have already been entered into the grid, to help you on your way.

6	4	25	23	■	13	9	13	9	23	■	5	3	4	16
3	■	■	6	3	9	■	23	■	10	■	■	10	■	23
7	4	13	23	■	26	4	10	10	20	20	■	9	■	15
10	■	■	12	■	10	■	9	■	■	13	26	8	4	13
■	■	22	20	1	3	■	8	4	12	19	■	■	13	■
2	19	9	■	3	■	24	■	8	■	9	16	16	20	14
23	■	6	■	13	19	23	15	21	26	■	■	14	■	20
17	14	4	18	21	■	8	■	24	■	23	18	4	6	20
20	■	23	■	■	20	12	14	20	18	18	■	17	■	6
14	20	13	23	10	■	15	■	16	■	19	■	15	23	26
■	26	■	■	9	7	20	8	■	16	26	10	20	■	■
14	20	15	23	11	■	■	4	■	4	■	3	■	■	19
23	■	23	■	26	23	2	8	20	6	■	16	23	21	20
4	■	13	■	■	26	■	16	■	23 A	8 N	16 T	■	■	23
6	3	21	20	■	20	16	19	26	15	■	26	23	14	6

A B C D E F G H I J K L M

N O P Q R S T U V W X Y Z

1	2	3	4	5	6	7	8 N	9	10	11	12	13
14	15	16 T	17	18	19	20	21	22	23 A	24	25	26

23   Jigsaw

Which four shapes (two black and two white) can be fitted together to form the elephant shown here? The pieces may be rotated, but not flipped over.

24   Criss Cross: Cake Baking

The words are provided, but can you fit them all into the grid?

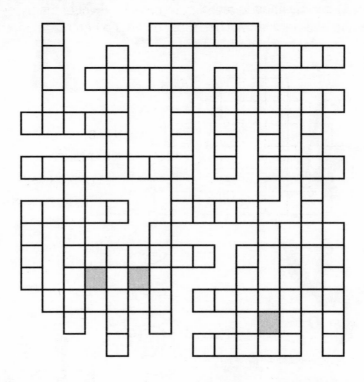

4 letters	MIXER	7 letters
BOWL	SPOON	BEATING
CAKE	SUGAR	LOAF TIN
EGGS	WATER	RAISINS
NUTS	YEAST	TESTING
TRAY		

6 letters   **8 letters**

5 letters	BUTTER	CHERRIES
AROMA	GRATER	CURRANTS
CREAM	RECIPE	DECORATE
FLOUR	SPONGE	
FRUIT		**9 letters**
ICING		PARCHMENT

25   Pyragram

Every clue in this puzzle is an anagram leading to a single-word solution. Correctly solve the anagram on each level of the pyramid and another word will appear, reading down the central column.

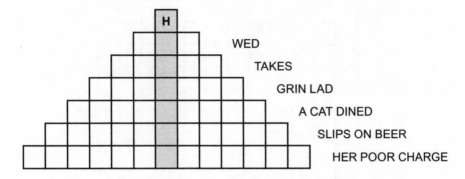

H

WED

TAKES

GRIN LAD

A CAT DINED

SLIPS ON BEER

HER POOR CHARGE

26   Word Ladder

Change one letter at a time (but not the position of any letter) to make a new word – and move from the word at the top of the ladder to the word at the bottom using the exact number of rungs provided.

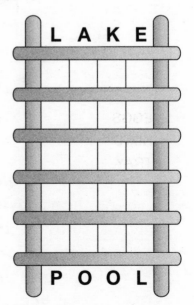

L A K E

P O O L

27   Skyscrapers

Place the numbers 1 to 5 into each row and column, one number per square. Each number represents a skyscraper of that many floors.

Arrange the skyscrapers in such a way that the given number outside the grid represents the number of buildings which can be seen from that point, looking only at that number's row or column.

A skyscraper with a lower number of floors cannot hide a higher building, but a one with a higher number of floors always hides any building behind it.

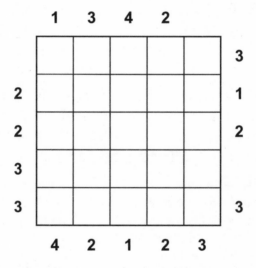

"Mindfulness is about love
and loving life. When you
cultivate this love, it gives you
clarity and compassion for
life, and your actions happen
in accordance with that."

Jon Kabat-Zinn

28   **Wordsearch:
A Midsummer Night's Dream**

Can you find all of the underlined words from this extract from
William Shakespeare's "A Midsummer Night's Dream" hidden in the
grid? Words run forward or backward, in either a horizontal, vertical,
or diagonal direction.

N	I	D	T	E	H	T	A	L	A	B	N	O
E	R	E	H	T	G	L	U	I	S	O	E	T
N	R	I	E	A	F	L	N	N	D	W	D	E
I	A	P	S	E	L	A	A	D	O	P	I	E
B	E	O	E	D	T	K	I	N	A	R	W	W
D	T	N	G	I	E	N	K	R	T	N	D	S
O	I	A	T	H	G	P	W	L	Y	I	A	P
O	U	C	S	W	O	R	H	T	U	K	N	E
W	Q	R	Y	E	E	M	Y	H	T	S	C	E
E	U	E	D	S	O	M	E	T	I	M	E	L
N	N	V	W	W	D	X	W	T	H	G	S	S
M	I	O	I	O	H	E	L	I	K	E	H	S
K	L	G	U	R	R	E	E	I	L	N	N	N
B	S	T	H	G	H	D	R	W	P	D	A	A
E	A	R	Y	T	H	A	V	E	Y	S	I	B

I know a bank where the wild thyme blows,

Where oxlips and the nodding violet grows,

Quite over-canopied with luscious woodbine,

With sweet musk-roses and with eglantine:

There sleeps Titania sometime of the night,

Lull'd in these flowers with dances and delight;

And there the snake throws her enamell'd skin,

Weed wide enough to wrap a fairy in…

No Three in Line

Place either O or X into each empty square, so that no three consecutive squares in either a horizontal row or vertical column contain more than two of the same symbol.

There needs to be as many Os as Xs in every row and column.

O		X		X	O		X
O			O			X	
	X			O			
O			X	O	X		O
X	X		O			O	
O			O			X	
	X			O		O	O
	X	O		O			

"Initially, whatever spiritual disciplines you may be practising are not real at all. You are just imagining yourself doing them. But that kind of limited deception and that kind of acting out have to be accepted as a stepping-stone. We have no other way of doing it. . . . We have to use poverty in order to become rich."

Chögyam Trungpa Rinpoche

Sudoku

Place one of the numbers from 1 to 9 into every empty cell so that each row, each column and each 3x3 block contains all the numbers from 1 to 9.

		7			2	1	9	
3	1	2	9					
	4			6	5			7
		5		8			1	4
		3	6		4	5		
2	7			1		8		
8			7	4			3	
					1	7	8	5
	2	9	8			6		

"Who among us hasn't
envied a cat's ability to
ignore the cares of daily life
and to relax completely?"

Karen Brademeyer

31   Combiku

Each horizontal row and vertical column should contain four different shapes, and four different numbers.

Every square will contain one number and one shape, and no combination may be repeated anywhere else in the puzzle; so, for instance, if a square contains a 3 and a star, then no other square containing a 3 will also contain a star, and no other square with a star will also contain a 3.

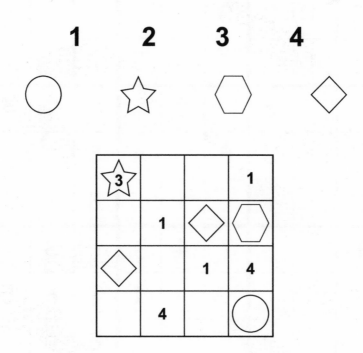

 "Yesterday is gone. Tomorrow has not yet come. We have only today. Let us begin."

Mother Teresa

Shadow Play

Which of the shadows is that of the pair of playful dolphins shown here?

A

C

B

D

E

F

G

33   Criss Cross: Flowers

The words are provided, but can you fit them all into the grid?

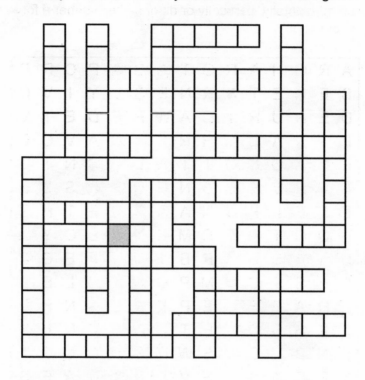

4 letters
IRIS
LILY

5 letters
DAISY
LILAC
LUPIN
STOCK
TANSY
TULIP

6 letters
CROCUS
DAHLIA
ORCHID
THRIFT
VIOLET

7 letters
ANEMONE
COWSLIP
GENTIAN

8 letters
BERGAMOT
CYCLAMEN
SCABIOUS
VALERIAN

9 letters
EDELWEISS
RUDBECKIA

10 letters
WALLFLOWER

34 Wordsearch: In the Greenhouse

Can you find all of the listed words hidden in the grid below? Words run horizontally, vertically or diagonally, in either a forward or backward direction.

```
A R G H A R O T A G A P O R P
S F K E T S R N E S L Y I V C
D E R U R I C A W P F D E T V
E T X A L M H R F I D A V O E
E L A O N O I T A L U S N I G
S F R M B C D N E C I H S L E
E L E L P U H A A R B E T H T
H O C T G E S M E T S L O Y A
C W A S S T R B I T I F E G B
O E S T C O M P O S T O L E L
L R A E F U E P E R E A N H E
C K S S C A R T O W S C N L S
E N B U O M S W M S H O U G T
I F C A S I E V E E I M A E S
U W A T E L L M S A U T E R F
```

BENCHES	GLASS	SHELF
BOXES	INSECTS	SIEVE
CLIPS	INSULATION	SOIL
CLOCHE	ORCHID	STAKE
COMPOST	POTS	TAGS
CUCUMBER	PROPAGATOR	TAMPER
FLOWER	RIDDLE	TROWEL
GERMINATION	SEEDS	VEGETABLES

Maze

Start at the top and find a path to the middle of the maze.

"The purpose of meditation
practice is not enlightenment;
it is to pay attention even at
unextraordinary times, to be of the
present, nothing-but-the-present,
to bear this mindfulness of now
into each event of ordinary life."

Peter Matthiessen

Logi-5

Every row and column of this grid should contain one each of the letters A, B, C, D, and E.

In addition, each of the five shapes (marked by thicker lines) should also contain one each of the letters A, B, C, D, and E.

Can you complete the grid?

		C	E	
	C	D		E
			C	
E		A		
	D			

"Like a child standing in
a beautiful park with his
eyes shut tight, there's
no need to imagine trees,
flowers, deer, birds, and
sky; we merely need to
open our eyes and realize
what is already here, who
we already are – as soon
as we stop pretending
we're small or unholy."

Bo Lozoff

Arroword

Solve the clues, then enter each answer in the direction of the arrows, one letter per square.

Accumulate	Dress worn primarily by Hindu women	▼	Away	▼	Undue partiality to one's relations	▼	Confused scuffle / Know (Scots) ▼
◣					Stretch ▶		▼
Overgrown with a clinging plant	By means of		Force / Clairvoyance (inits) ▶				
◣	▼		▼		A single / Greek letter ▶		
Look with amazement		Dissenting clique / Smart alec (coll) ▶			▼		Beverage
◣		▼		Conspicuous success / Back end ▶		▼	Involuntary expulsion of air from the nose
Temporary police force	Sound off		Gets up / Glances over ▶	▼			▼
◣	▼		▼		Adult male person / Common amphibian ▶		
Nut / Tube of tobacco in paper ▶					▼	Archaic form of the word 'your'	Gratuity
◣						▼	▼
Holy sister / Devices which fit locks ▶				Buzzing sound ▶			
◣				Printed characters ▶			

Sudoku

Place one of the numbers from 1 to 9 into every empty cell so that each row, each column and each 3x3 block contains all the numbers from 1 to 9.

	9	5			7	3		
		6	8		3		4	
				4	6	2	7	
3				2	4			5
1		9				4		2
2			9	3				6
	4	2	3	5				
	7		1		9	8		
		8	4			9	5	

"When I let go of
what I am, I become
what I might be."

Lao Tzu

39   Codeword

Every letter in this puzzle has been replaced by a number, the number remaining the same for that letter wherever it occurs. Every letter of the alphabet has been used. Substitute numbers for letters to complete the codeword.

It may help to cross off the letters beneath the grid to keep a track of progress, and to use the reference box showing which numbers have been decoded. Three letters have already been entered into the grid, to help you on your way.

13	22	3	15	11	23	■	6	11	2	23	20	11	10	14
14		9	■	18	■	■	8	■	1	■	5	■	■	22
2	23	23	22	19	11	23	■	8	■	5	11	7	1	18
12	■	22	■	22	■	2	18	11	18	22	■	22	■	18
16	15	26	20	23	22	7	■	2	■	23	11	18	10	22
11	■	■	2	■	10	1	11	5	13	22	■	10	■	23
10	23	2	18	10	24	■	7(D)	■	6	2	7	9	■	
14	■	■	19	■	1	3	2(I)	7	22	■	2	■	■	20
	16	1	14	22	■	■	22(E)	■	5	11	21	11	19	22
25	■	11	■	11	7	7	15	10	22	■	11	■	■	8
15	12	13	22	6	■	11	■	9	1	15	18	19	22	5
11	■	26	■	9	11	4	18	13	■	13	■	5	■	2
2	21	2	22	7	■	7	■	6	5	11	12	22	17	22
18	■	18	■	2	■	23	■	■	19	■	22	■	■	18
6	5	22	18	7	2	22	5	■	21	22	18	6	22	7

A B C D E F G H I J K L M
N O P Q R S T U V W X Y Z

1	2 (I)	3	4	5	6	7 (D)	8	9	10	11	12	13
14	15	16	17	18	19	20	21	22 (E)	23	24	25	26

40   Wordsearch: Birthday Party

Can you find all of the listed words hidden in the grid below?
Words run horizontally, vertically or diagonally, in either a forward or
backward direction.

```
S W E R Y A N S T E R A L B E
E I S K D L E C E U Y E A P M
L S M U N T I S W P M S X P E
D R K A A O P M P X S T M A H
N E J L E E I A A E R F A P T
A N P B E R H T S F R I R E E
C N Y C R U C S A I O G Q R S
U A H A E L A E E T L B U H I
A B E C O L C N C C I D E A R
C E R W G J D W E I A V E T P
E I N W I S H E S S A R N S R
I D S E M A G U E S T S D I U
P L A U G H T E R B K K P S S
E K E M M B E B A L L O O N S
Y U S E K A C R I N A S E L E
```

BALLOONS	GAMES	MARQUEE
BANNERS	GIFTS	MUSIC
CAKES	GLASSES	PAPER HATS
CANDLES	GUESTS	PLATES
CARDS	HAPPY	SPEECH
CLOWN	ICE CREAM	SURPRISE
FAMILY	INVITATION	THEME
FRIENDS	LAUGHTER	WISHES

41   Coin Collecting

In this puzzle, an amateur coin collector has been out with his metal detector, searching for booty. He didn't have time to dig up all the coins he found, so has made a grid map, showing their locations, in the hope that if he loses the map, at least no-one else will understand it... However, he didn't count on YOU coming across the strange grid (as seen here). Will you be able to discover the correct number of coins and their precise locations?

Those squares containing numbers are empty, but where a number appears in a square, it indicates how many coins are located in the squares (up to a maximum of eight) surrounding the numbered one, touching it at any corner or side. There is only one coin in any individual square.

Place a circle into every square containing a coin.

1	1	2		2	1		1
2				4		4	
2			2				2
	3	2			5	5	
	2		1	1			
2					2	5	
	2			1	2	3	
2							2

"Doing the best at this moment puts you in the best place for the next moment."

Oprah Winfrey

Flower Power

Fit the listed words into the grid below, then rearrange the letters in the shaded squares to form another word related to the theme of this book.

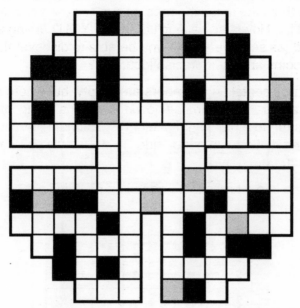

3 letters	**4 letters**		**5 letters**	
ACT	BEAK	LOAF	ARGON	INCUR
ADO	BIAS	ONUS	AVERT	LASSO
BUS	BOSS	PUMP	BLAZE	MANGO
BUT	BYTE	SHOP	COWER	RATIO
CRY	EMIR	STEW	CRUEL	SMELT
ROE	LINK	YOGA	FLUTE	TUTOR
TUG				
WIN				

"Every thought we think is creating our future."

Louise Hay

43   Patchwork

Every square should be filled with a letter from A to D, and each heavily outlined set of four squares should contain four different letters. Every row and column must contain two of each letter.

Squares that share a common border may not contain the same letter.

			A	C		D	C
		B			C		
C	D		B			A	
D	B			B			
		C		D	C		
				A			
		A				C	
C	B		A		B		A

"When we meditate we expand, spreading our wings like a bird, trying to enter consciously into Infinity, Eternity and Immortality, welcoming them into our aspiring consciousness."

Sri Chinmoy

44   Slitherlink

Draw a single continuous loop, by connecting the dots. No line may cross the path of another.

The figure inside each set of any four surrounding dots indicates the total number of surrounding lines.

```
.  .  .  .  .  .  .  .  .  .  .
  2  2  2  2  2     1  2  2
.  .  .  .  .  .  .  .  .  .  .
  2     2  3  2  3  3  3  2
.  .  .  .  .  .  .  .  .  .  .
        2        1  1  1
.  .  .  .  .  .  .  .  .  .  .
  2  2  1  2  0  1  2  2
.  .  .  .  .  .  .  .  .  .  .
 1           3  3     2
.  .  .  .  .  .  .  .  .  .  .
  2     1     2  1
.  .  .  .  .  .  .  .  .  .  .
 2  2  3  3              2
.  .  .  .  .  .  .  .  .  .  .
  2  1     1  2  2  2
.  .  .  .  .  .  .  .  .  .  .
 3     3  3  3  2  3  2
.  .  .  .  .  .  .  .  .  .  .
```

"I come into the peace of wild things who do not tax their lives with forethought of grief. I come into the presence of still water. And I feel above me the day-blind stars waiting with their light. For a time I rest in the grace of the world, and am free."

Wendell Berry

45

Arroword

Solve the clues, then enter each answer in the direction of the arrows, one letter per square.

Garments such as coats, scarves, hats, etc	Not mature (of fruit)	Those people	▼	Fewer	▼	Not having permission to desert one's post (inits)	▼	Sauce to accompany Mexican food
▼	▼	▼						
British system of medical care (inits) ▶				Also		Mistake		Brush
Edgy ▶				▼		▼		▼
▶			Stick fruit		Uncooked ▶			
Aspire ▶		Bellow ▶	▼				Large North American deer	
▶				Seize suddenly	Be in debt ▶		▼	
Engage as gears ▶	Profes-sional cook	Remove packaging ▶		▼				
▶	▼				Costa Rican capital, ___ José	Conclude		Ignited
Aqualung ▶		Descend by rope ▶			▼	▼		▼
▶				Against ▶				
Carry		Brigand ▶						

Wordsearch: Swimming Pool

Can you find all of the listed words hidden in the grid below? Words run horizontally, vertically or diagonally, in either a forward or backward direction.

T	A	M	F	T	N	A	D	N	E	T	T	A	P	E
R	W	S	E	Y	M	J	A	W	U	A	R	S	F	R
E	H	S	A	L	P	S	B	K	K	E	I	O	A	M
T	I	E	D	R	A	U	G	E	F	I	L	L	D	S
A	S	L	E	Y	L	A	A	R	W	D	R	A	I	N
W	T	C	L	A	D	D	E	R	N	W	A	R	B	O
F	L	S	E	Y	I	S	G	X	S	H	O	W	E	R
T	E	U	A	P	H	N	E	E	E	S	I	A	P	K
R	L	M	P	M	I	I	D	M	C	R	A	W	L	E
U	A	G	E	T	C	I	S	M	U	A	C	Z	E	L
N	E	N	A	E	L	G	R	C	I	T	F	I	V	R
K	T	O	B	S	S	L	E	W	O	T	S	K	S	A
S	L	S	E	H	G	W	S	Y	S	T	R	O	K	E
F	L	U	M	E	P	B	O	Y	T	R	A	P	C	J
M	A	T	T	E	O	S	P	V	E	R	A	N	E	G

ATTENDANT

BRAWN

COSTUME

CRAWL

DRAIN

EXERCISE

FLOATING

FLUME

LADDER

LIFEGUARD

MUSCLE

PARTY

POSERS

REFRESH-
MENTS

SHOWER

SLIDES

SNORKEL

SPLASH

STROKE

TAKE A DIP

TOWELS

TRUNKS

WATER

WHISTLE

47   Codeword

Every letter in this puzzle has been replaced by a number, the number remaining the same for that letter wherever it occurs. Every letter of the alphabet has been used. Substitute numbers for letters to complete the codeword.

It may help to cross off the letters beneath the grid to keep a track of progress, and to use the reference box showing which numbers have been decoded. Three letters have already been entered into the grid, to help you on your way.

18	12	1	21	20	2		11	8	9	18	21	1	9	9
12		3		6		14		18		12		26		25
1	17	1	20	18		24	25	18	23	24	26	6	21	16
1		16		6	21	13		6		3		9		8
18	1	8		4		1	9	20	8	3	8	18	24	12
24		21		1			1		5		15		21	
5	8	18	1	21	18	1	7		12	8	19	19	6	18
	7		21		1		25		24		1		24	
10	24	24	7	1	21		20	24	21	23	12	24	21	18
	12		24		1		1			24		11		12
9	21	24	10	9	18	24	12	15		25		1	14	1
22		8		20		23		24	10	21		12		8
25	21	13	21 N	24 O	18 T	18	1	7		7	12	1	8	7
6		1		10		1		1		1		8		3
19	25	21	16	3	6	21	16		10	12	6	18	2	1

A B C D E F G H I J K L M

N O P Q R S T U V W X Y Z

1	2	3	4	5	6	7	8	9	10	11	12	13
14	15	16	17	18 T	19	20	21 N	22	23	24 O	25	26

48   Sudoku

Place one of the numbers from 1 to 9 into every empty cell so that each row, each column and each 3x3 block contains all the numbers from 1 to 9.

			6	3	2			
	1	8		7			4	3
	6					7		5
		1	7			4	5	2
6			3		4			7
4	7	9			1	8		
7		5					1	
3	8			1		2	6	
			4	9	3			

"If you wait for tomorrow, tomorrow comes. If you don't wait for tomorrow, tomorrow comes."

Senegalese proverb

49   Criss Cross: Time for Bed

The words are provided, but can you fit them all into the grid?

3 letters	6 letters	8 letters
BED	DOZING	MATTRESS
COT	PILLOW	
	SHEETS	9 letters
4 letters	SLEEPY	NIGHTGOWN
BATH	SNOOZE	UNDRESSED
LAMP	WARMTH	
REST		10 letters
SNUG	7 letters	ALARM CLOCK
YAWN	COMFORT	
	LULLABY	
5 letters	PRAYERS	
COCOA	SNORING	
RELAX	WASHING	

Calcudoku

Each row and column should contain different numbers from 1 to 6.

The numbers placed in a heavily outlined set of squares may be repeated, but must produce the calculation in the top left corner, using the mathematical symbol provided: multiply (x), divide (/), add (+), and subtract (–).

For example, when multiplied, the numbers 4 and 3 total 12:

12x	
4	**3**

4/		1–		11+	
2/		15x	3/	5+	
60x				8x	2/
	6/		100x		
2/	8+				2/
	9+		3/		

"The entire world is an open book, a scripture. Read it. Learn while digging a pit or chopping some wood or cooking some food. If you can't learn from your daily activities, how are you going to understand the scriptures?"

Swami Satchidananda

51

Bridges

Join the circular islands by drawing horizontal or vertical lines to represent bridges, in such a way that the number of bridges connected to each island must match the number on that island. No bridge may cross another, and no more than two bridges can join any pair of islands.

The finished design will allow you to travel from one island to any other island on the map.

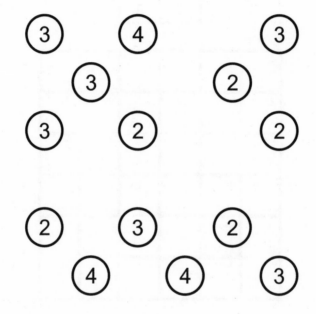

"Each moment is a chance
for us to make peace
with the world, to make
peace possible for the
world, to make happiness
possible for the world."

Thich Nhat Hanh

52   Wordsearch: Movies

Can you find all of the listed words hidden in the grid below?
Words run horizontally, vertically or diagonally, in either a forward or
backward direction.

```
S P U D N C A I D O Z S E R A
R T R Y R O T S Y O T L N A S
E T B E N E O U L R Y R O P T
T Z O D I A S T L P N I I N E
S S I L E N C E A A U G T U R
I J E Z E B E L F L H L I G A
S U E D A M A H Y E P A N P I
N O R B I T A S K R F I O O N
L T E T B S S C S I E R M T M
F E F V H E T H L D D E E O A
T R R T S A A U N E V T R O N
E A O N A M R O R R B A P T L
R B S Z P C R V F B C M E S I
O A H O E A E R E N I E W I D
S C O I L N A N D Y R A G E E
```

AMADEUS	MATERIAL GIRLS	SISTERS
CABARET	NORBIT	SKYFALL
CAMELOT	PALE RIDER	TOOTSIE
DISTURBIA	PLATOON	TOP GUN
FROZEN	PREMONITION	TOY STORY
HARVEY	RAIN MAN	ULYSSES
JEZEBEL	SHAMPOO	WEINER
LA RONDE	SILENCE	ZODIAC

53   Arroword

Solve the clues, then enter each answer in the direction of the arrows, one letter per square.

Colla-borator with an occupying force ▼	▼	Dull pain	▼	Expanse	▼	Tube ___ Things of value ▼	___ and outs
►		▼				▼	Stomach
Defender ___ Coat with sugar ►			Exclama-tion ___ Divisions of a week ►				▼
Shelters from light ►			▼			Hinged section of a table	
►		Alien		Deciduous tree ►		▼	
Alcoholic beverage	Arrange-ment ▼						
►				Allege ►			
Biting flies	Naked		Law passed by Parliament	▼	Vagrant		Creeping or crawling inverte-brates
Broken husks of the seeds of cereal grains	Collection of things ___ Angry dispute ▼	▼				Impene-trable mist ▼	▼
►	▼		Bean curd ►				
Debau-chery ___ Affectedly dainty ►				Wet spongy ground ►			
►			Garments ►				

Sudoku

Place one of the numbers from 1 to 9 into every empty cell so that each row, each column and each 3x3 block contains all the numbers from 1 to 9.

9			1		2			3
	2	4		9	7			5
		7				1		2
	1	6	2	8				
	9		6		3		4	
				7	4	5	6	
8		1				3		
6			8	5		7	2	
5			4		6			9

"Silence fertilizes the deep place where personality grows. A life with a peaceful centre can weather all storms."

Norman Vincent Peale

55 Codeword

Every letter in this puzzle has been replaced by a number, the number remaining the same for that letter wherever it occurs. Every letter of the alphabet has been used. Substitute numbers for letters to complete the codeword.

It may help to cross off the letters beneath the grid to keep a track of progress, and to use the reference box showing which numbers have been decoded. Three letters have already been entered into the grid, to help you on your way.

13	15	14	14	19	22	3	5		17	22	19	17	6	14 **E**
	11		18		23		23	1	14		14			3 **N**
14	25	12	11	2	11	17	14		11	20	11	13	14	26 **D**
	1		17		17		11			6		12		
20		23	14	9	14	12	17	6	23	1		11	23	10
23		14		11		23		2		9		23		11
6	20	21	14	12	17	22	2	14		23	14	22	5	3
15		6		14		10		23		22		9		11
13	24	22	10	19		13	7	16	14	14	8	22	3	5
14		3		11		6		13		3		14		14
23	6	26		12	6	3	17	14	3	26	14	23		23
		14		24			11		11		23		5	
4	11	23	11	13	13		19	11	13	13	11	20	18	14
6			18		11	5	14		11		13		14	
19	11	18	18	22	26		23	14	18	22	14	2	14	26

A B C D E F G H I J K L M

N O P Q R S T U V W X Y Z

1	2	3 **N**	4	5	6	7	8	9	10	11	12	13
14 **E**	15	16	17	18	19	20	21	22	23	24	25	26 **D**

Jigsaw

Which four shapes (two black and two white) can be fitted together to form the cat shown here? The pieces may be rotated, but not flipped over.

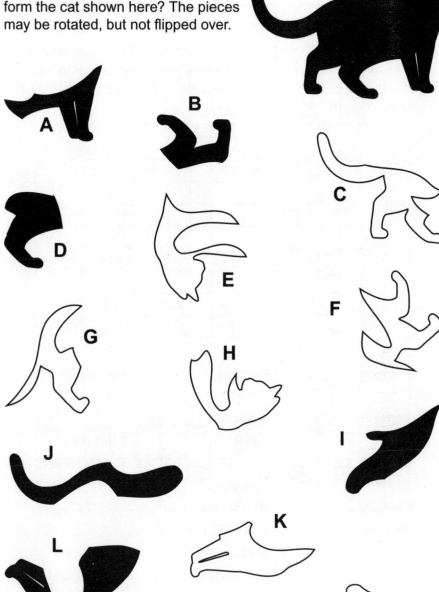

57   Criss Cross: Varieties of Apple

The words are provided, but can you fit them all into the grid?

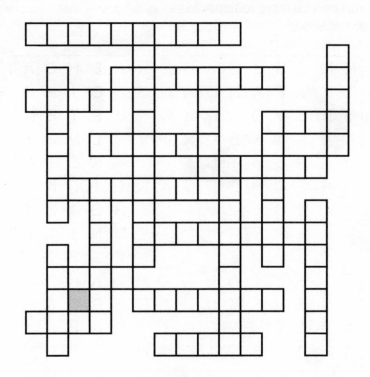

4 letters
COX'S
ENVY
JAZZ
KATY

5 letters
AKANE
MUTSU
SONYA

6 letters
FIESTA
HAWAII
IDARED

7 letters
ALKMENE
CARROLL
MALINDA
WAGENER
WEALTHY

8 letters
CATSHEAD

9 letters
DISCOVERY
EDWARD VII
ST CECILIA

10 letters
HONEYCRISP

11 letters
CHARLES ROSS

58   Wordsearch: Shades of Pink

Can you find all of the listed words hidden in the grid below?
Words run horizontally, vertically or diagonally, in either a forward or
backward direction.

```
H M O S S O L B Y R R E H C A
T Y J F A N D A N G O O I B P
N R E V O L G X O F E E T E R
A R A W R E D N E V A L M E I
R E W C H I N A P I N K S I C
A B S C H E D D A R P I N K O
M W K O A N M A C C R O A S T
A A G P L R A V I E N N I A A
P R U N O F N I C N P E S I M
P T E L I W E A L M P A H S A
E S R N T K D R T U E R C A R
A P A T U R C E I I H G U L I
C E R I S V A O R N O T F M S
H A T N E G A M H D O N N O K
N A I S R E P R O S E P I N K
```

AMARANTH	FOXGLOVE	ROSE PINK
APRICOT	FUCHSIA	SALMON
CARNATION	LAVENDER	SHOCKING
CERISE	MAGENTA	SOLFERINO
CHEDDAR PINK	PEACH	STRAWBERRY
CHERRY BLOSSOM	PEONY	TAMARISK
	PERSIAN	THULIAN
CHINA PINK	POWDER	ULTRA
FANDANGO		

59   No Four in Line

Place either O or X into each empty square, so that no four consecutive squares in a straight line in any direction (horizontally, vertically, or diagonally) contain more than three of the same symbol.

O	X		O		O	O	O	
	O	O	O			O	O	
X		O		O			O	X
	X			O		X		
		O	O			X		
X		O		O			O	
		X				O		X
O		X	X	X		O	X	X
X	O	X				X	X	X

"Mindfulness provides the most simple and direct, the most thorough and effective method for training and developing the mind for its daily tasks and problems."

Nyanaponika Thera

60   Pyragram

Every clue in this puzzle is an anagram leading to a single-word solution. Correctly solve the anagram on each level of the pyramid and another word will appear, reading down the central column.

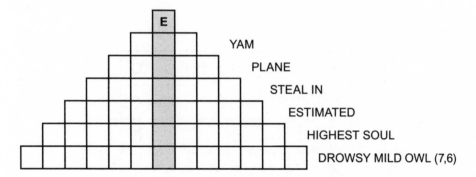

YAM
PLANE
STEAL IN
ESTIMATED
HIGHEST SOUL
DROWSY MILD OWL (7,6)

61   Word Wheel

How many words of three or more letters can you make from those in the wheel, without using plurals, abbreviations or proper nouns?

The central letter must appear once in every word and no letter in a section of the wheel may be used more than once.

There is at least one nine-letter word in the wheel.

Nine-letter word(s):

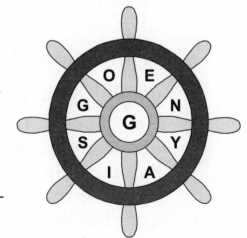

_____

Fill the grid so that every horizontal row and vertical column contains all the numbers 1 to 6.

Any arrows in the grid always point toward a square that contains a lower number.

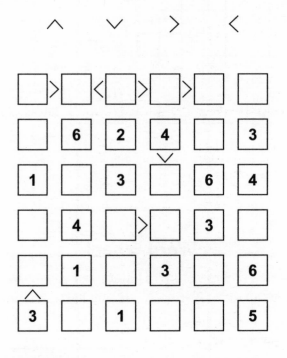

"If you come from a place of love then you are free and fear dispels itself into nothing. If you live in the moment – in the present – then you don't fear because you can let all the good, the miracles, in."

Cat Forsley

63 **Sudoku**

Place one of the numbers from 1 to 9 into every empty cell so that each row, each column and each 3x3 block contains all the numbers from 1 to 9.

					7		5	6
5		2		9	3		8	
	6	7			2	3		
		5			4		6	1
8			2		6			7
1	4		8			9		
		1	3			4	2	
	2		7	5		1		3
9	8		4					

"No valid plans for the future
can be made by those who have
no capacity for living now."

Alan Watts

64   Domino Placement

A standard set of 28 dominoes has been laid out as shown. Can you draw in the edges of them all?

The check-box is provided as an aid, so that you can see which dominoes have been located.

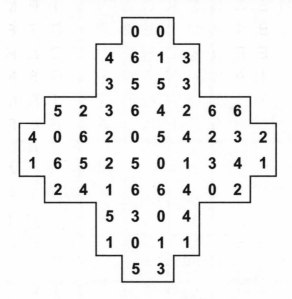

0-0	0-1	0-2	0-3	0-4	0-5	0-6	1-1	1-2	1-3	1-4	1-5	1-6	2-2

2-3	2-4	2-5	2-6	3-3	3-4	3-5	3-6	4-4	4-5	4-6	5-5	5-6	6-6

"No age is too early or too late for the health of the soul."

Epicurus

65   Wordsearch: Marine Life

Can you find all of the listed words hidden in the grid below? Words run horizontally, vertically or diagonally, in either a forward or backward direction.

```
E M E S C E K C O D D I P M E
S A B A R U L E B D K D T B S
R N E E U K D H C N O C A H U
O A I A S K N A R P L R S N R
H T R I T O N U O A N I R M K
A E H A A T H R H A F E I R A
E E E B C L T W C E T E A O R
S S L R E S R L L S B H O W A
W H G S A A E T B A S N T P S
I R S G N I T O E K V E M I P
A U A E T U L O V B P E U H M
M Z N C C O R A L M A D R S I
L L I R K A S T I O N T E C R
L O R R A B A L O N E T X P H
A F F O L L E H S K S U T E S
```

ABALONE	LAVER	SEAHORSE
BARNACLE	LIMPET	SHARK
CONCH	LOBSTER	SHIPWORM
CORAL	MANATEE	SHRIMP
CRUSTACEAN	MUREX	TRITON
CUTTLEFISH	MUSSEL	TUSK SHELL
GASTROPOD	NARWHAL	VOLUTE
KRILL	PIDDOCK	WRACK

66   Criss Cross: Herbs and Spices

The words are provided, but can you fit them all into the grid?

4 letters
MACE
SAGE

5 letters
ANISE
CAPER
CUMIN
SENNA
THYME

6 letters
CASSIA
FENNEL
GARLIC
HYSSOP
LOVAGE
SORREL

7 letters
CATMINT
CAYENNE
CHERVIL
MUSTARD

8 letters
MARJORAM

9 letters
CORIANDER
HYPERICUM
LEMON BALM

11 letters
HORSERADISH
ST JOHN'S
  WORT

67   Flower Power

Fit the listed words into the grid below, then rearrange the letters in the shaded squares to form another word related to the theme of this book.

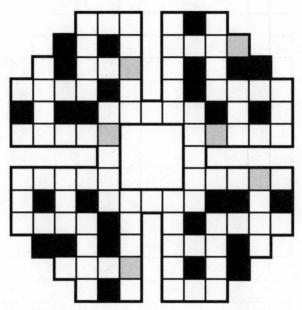

3 letters	4 letters		5 letters	
AIM	AFAR	PACK	ASKEW	SALTY
AWL	BOLD	PLAY	GHOST	SCOOP
JAB	DAME	SNUG	GLOWS	SWISS
JUT	DEFT	TAXI	JEANS	TOWEL
NOW	JUNE	TICK	MIRTH	TRUSS
NUN	JURY	YAWN	RETRY	WOMAN
OIL				
PRY				

"The brain is wider than the sky."

Emily Dickinson

68   **Maze**

Start at the top and find a path to the middle of the maze.

"When you follow your bliss
. . . doors will open where
you would not have thought
there would be doors; and
where there wouldn't be a
door for anyone else."

Joseph Campbell

In Place

Place the listed words horizontally into the grid, so that when read from top left to bottom right, the letters in the shaded squares spell out a word linked to the theme of this book. Some letters are already in place.

ADMIRAL

CRUMBLE

GALLERY

HAMMOCK

PERFECT

SCARLET

WORKBOX

		U				
				B		
		L				
				L		

"Don't worry about what the world needs. Ask what makes you come alive and do that. Because what the world needs is people who have come alive."

Howard Thurman

70   Arroword

Solve the clues, then enter each answer in the direction of the arrows, one letter per square.

			Pretty knot				Piece of music played at a marriage (7,5)	Cubes of meat cooked on a skewer
Start again		Tungsten	Latin: 'and elsewhere' (2,2)					
Large container for liquids					Expression of surprise or alarm			
One whose age has impaired his mind							Farewell	
				In this particular place (4,4)	Light touch or stroke			
South American hunting rope with weights	'Sunshine State' of the USA							
Collect discarded material	Basement		Sight		Pen point			
								Currency
Independent ruler or chieftain					Informal term for a mother			
Golden ___, record popular in past times		Branch of orthodox Islam					Wing of an insect	
					Directed or controlled			
Salt water		Shrine where a god is consulted						
					Fodder			

Wordsearch: Rivers of Africa

Can you find all of the listed words hidden in the grid below?
Words run horizontally, vertically or diagonally, in either a forward or
backward direction.

U	J	U	R	I	G	N	A	B	U	E	S	E	Y	A
G	E	U	E	P	A	U	O	N	I	L	A	H	Y	A
T	R	U	B	H	E	A	C	A	V	A	L	L	A	W
I	U	A	T	B	A	R	A	H	K	W	A	N	G	O
M	C	R	E	G	A	U	O	Z	I	M	T	L	L	M
A	U	U	B	A	N	E	I	T	D	G	L	R	U	E
M	A	V	O	E	Z	S	E	V	U	P	O	P	A	R
O	N	U	U	F	V	N	O	L	A	P	V	R	P	E
L	D	M	R	Z	I	I	A	O	U	R	A	P	T	G
K	O	A	E	E	A	G	L	U	T	C	E	M	N	I
C	U	D	G	L	E	M	W	L	C	M	Z	G	I	N
O	B	N	R	N	A	L	B	M	E	L	A	A	A	S
N	E	A	E	E	L	I	N	E	U	L	B	G	S	K
G	H	S	G	N	C	A	T	E	Z	I	M	B	A	A
O	T	E	G	H	E	L	L	I	U	I	R	Y	E	S

ATBARAH	JUBBA	OTEGHELLI
BLUE NILE	KAGERA	RUVUMA
BOU REGREG	KUNENE	SAINT PAUL
CAVALLA	KWANGO	SENEGAL
CONGO	LOMAMI	TURBEVILLE
CUANDO	MAPUTO	UBANGI
CUANZA	NIGER	VOLTA
GAMTOOS	ONILAHY	ZAMBEZI

Codeword

Every letter in this puzzle has been replaced by a number, the number remaining the same for that letter wherever it occurs. Every letter of the alphabet has been used. Substitute numbers for letters to complete the codeword.

It may help to cross off the letters beneath the grid to keep a track of progress, and to use the reference box showing which numbers have been decoded. Three letters have already been entered into the grid, to help you on your way.

13	26	20	18	25	5		21		20		24	1	20	16
26		1		14		1	9	23	1	26	7			20
7	25	15	14	9	3	7	8		5		24	14	21	9
13		14		10		19		18	21	23	24			18
13	21	26	16	14	2	1	1	15			26	21	12	25
	10				1			1	5	9	14			5
9	21	23	16	2	21	3	17	26	14		5	21	8	14
	18		14		22		18		25		7		7	
6	26	7	23		14	23	6	26	1	20	23	14	25	8
18			21	12	9	20			23				18	
4	7	18	6			8	1	26	14	9	21	25	3	14
7			2	7	16	2		18		7		1		25
21	26	8	1		18		11	21 (A)	18 (I)	26 (L)	24	18	9	15
25			9	21	8	2	14	9		14		16		14
8	21	17	14		14		8		13	9	18	14	25	15

A B C D E F G H I J K L M
N O P Q R S T U V W X Y Z

1	2	3	4	5	6	7	8	9	10	11	12	13
14	15	16	17	18 (I)	19	20	21 (A)	22	23	24	25	26 (L)

Sudoku

Place one of the numbers from 1 to 9 into every empty cell so that each row, each column and each 3x3 block contains all the numbers from 1 to 9.

2			7		3			
5			4	6	8			
7				9		8	3	5
		5	9		2		4	
3		6				9		1
	2		3		6	5		
4	1	8		2				7
			8	7	5			4
			1		4			9

"Tension is who you think you should be. Relaxation is who you are."

Chinese proverb

74   Criss Cross: Wedding Day

The words are provided, but can you fit them all into the grid?

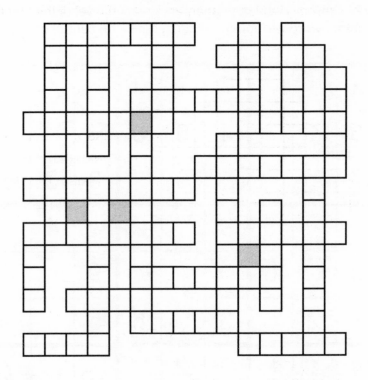

4 letters
CARS
VOWS
WIFE

5 letters
AISLE
ALTAR
BRIDE
DRESS
PAGES
RINGS
ROSES

TIARA
TRAIN
VICAR

6 letters
CAMERA
GARTER
SMILES

7 letters
BEST MAN
HUSBAND
SERVICE

8 letters
CEREMONY
CONFETTI
FREESIAS

9 letters
BETROTHED
CELEBRATE
TELEGRAMS

10 letters
BUTTONHOLE

75   Pyragram

Every clue in this puzzle is an anagram leading to a single-word solution. Correctly solve the anagram on each level of the pyramid and another word will appear, reading down the central column.

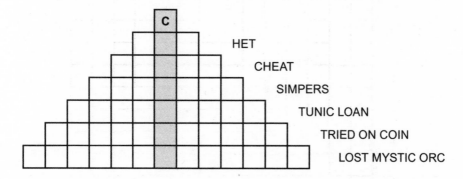

HET

CHEAT

SIMPERS

TUNIC LOAN

TRIED ON COIN

LOST MYSTIC ORC

76   Word Ladder

Change one letter at a time (but not the position of any letter) to make a new word – and move from the word at the top of the ladder to the word at the bottom using the exact number of rungs provided.

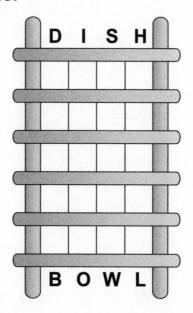

Number Link

Working from one square to another, horizontally or vertically (never diagonally), draw single continuous paths to pair up each set of two matching numbers.

No line may cross another, none may travel through any square containing a number, and every square must be visited just once.

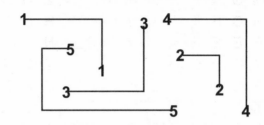

8						6	10	2
	7	4						
	1		1					
	11				7			
		3						
		5			6	2	10	
			11		4			
		5	3					12
8				12	9			9

"Awareness in itself is healing."

Frederick Salomon Perls

Wordsearch:
Moonlight, Summer Moonlight

Can you find all of the underlined words from the poem "Moonlight, Summer Moonlight" by Emily Brontë hidden in the grid? Words run forward or backward, in either a horizontal, vertical, or diagonal direction.

```
M O R F E W F R L R Z D S
G O E T I A U O T E H N E
A E F E A V V G R M N U E
R O N G R E T I U M T O S
S L M T L E A S E U E R D
T Y E Y L F H L O S E E A
Y S E N L Y O T E M W M E
D K S C D S B H O S S E H
L O S H H I T O T R E E S
I I L G E A N E W H E S R
W H U A E L E G D E A A E
I O I R I P T A R R R S W
B E B G E D E E G E O S O
L V H D H O U R R H E S L
S T A P T L L I T S D N F
```

'Tis <u>moonlight</u>, <u>summer</u> moonlight,
All <u>soft</u> and <u>still</u> and <u>fair</u>;
The <u>solemn</u> <u>hour</u> of midnight
<u>Breathes</u> <u>sweet</u> thoughts everywhere,

But <u>most</u> where <u>trees</u> are sending
Their breezy <u>boughs</u> on <u>high</u>,
Or stooping low are <u>lending</u>
A <u>shelter</u> <u>from</u> the <u>sky</u>.

And <u>there</u> in <u>those</u> <u>wild</u> <u>bowers</u>
A <u>lovely</u> <u>form</u> is <u>laid</u>;
<u>Green</u> <u>grass</u> and <u>dew-steeped</u> <u>flowers</u>
<u>Wave</u> <u>gently</u> <u>round</u> her <u>head</u>.

79   Arroword

Solve the clues, then enter each answer in the direction of the arrows, one letter per square.

Continues with one's activities	▼	Very dark black	▼	Continent	▼	Prejudice / Leafy vegetables	▼	Lease
┏		▼				▼		Junk
Social standing / Kimono sash ▶				Painting, sculpture, music, etc / Attack ▶				▼
Crude ▶				▼			By an unknown author, in short	
┏			Meat from a deer		Head of corn ▶		▼	
Under-stand (Scots)		Capital of Austria ▶	▼					
┏					Con-cession given to mollify ▶			
Summed up		Slender double-reed instrument		Sleeping place	▼	Lower part of an interior wall		Tatters
Curtsies	Greased / Be in debt ▶	▼				▼	Foot digit	▼
┗	▼			Facts given ▶			▼	
Timber / Was present, is now gone ▶					Canine creature ▶			
┗				Carries out ▶				

Sudoku

Place one of the numbers from 1 to 9 into every empty cell so that each row, each column and each 3x3 block contains all the numbers from 1 to 9.

4	6			9	7		2	
		8		3			1	6
9	3	5	1					
			4	2		7		
5		2				1		4
		7		5	8			
					6	3	7	9
3	2			8		4		
	1		9	4			8	5

"We shape clay
into a pot, but it
is the emptiness
inside that holds
whatever we want."

Lao Tzu

81   Codeword

Every letter in this puzzle has been replaced by a number, the number remaining the same for that letter wherever it occurs. Every letter of the alphabet has been used. Substitute numbers for letters to complete the codeword.

It may help to cross off the letters beneath the grid to keep a track of progress, and to use the reference box showing which numbers have been decoded. Three letters have already been entered into the grid, to help you on your way.

12	9	7	12	10	16	10	14	9		9		17		11
18			23		6		9			11	4	4	20	9	12
11	26	13	24	16	11	7	16	12		10		11		4
19			16		7			17	11	16	11	6	6	18
9	21	17	18	9	2	24	9	6		23		10 I		5
7			9		24			9	20	8		23 O		21
	15	23	6	17	10	25	20	9		9	7	7 N	24	10
9			20		20		5		12		23			11
4	23	20	5	4		4	9	26	11	7	16	10	17	
10		23		9	6	11			6		23			23
20		22		6		1	10	7	26	4	6	23	23	15
9	21	9	17	24	16	9			23		10			15
4		7		12		6	11	10	7	17	23	11	16	12
12	10	3	7	11	20		10		10		24			9
5		9		20		25	20	11	17	19	12	4	23	16

A B C D E F G H I J K L M

N O P Q R S T U V W X Y Z

1	2	3	4	5	6	7 N	8	9	10 I	11	12	13
14	15	16	17	18	19	20	21	22	23 O	24	25	26

82   **Reflections**

Which of the designs below is an exact horizontal (left to right) mirror image of the design to the right?

I

2

3

4

5

6

7

8

83   Criss Cross: Wood Types

The words are provided, but can you fit them all into the grid?

3 letters
ASH
ELM
FIR
OAK
YEW

4 letters
DEAL
PINE
TEAK

5 letters
ALDER
BALSA
BEECH
BRIAR
HAZEL
LARCH
MAPLE
OLIVE

6 letters
POPLAR
WICKER

7 letters
JUNIPER
REDWOOD

8 letters
CHESTNUT
MAHOGANY
ROSEWOOD
SANDARAC
SYCAMORE

10 letters
EUCALYPTUS
GRANADILLA

84   Light Up

Place circles (representing light bulbs) in some of the empty squares, in such a way that no two bulbs shine on each other, until every square of the grid is lit up. A bulb sends rays of light horizontally and vertically, illuminating its entire row and column unless its light is blocked by a black cell.

Some black cells contain numbers, indicating how many light bulbs are in adjacent squares either immediately above, below, to the right, or to the left. Bulbs placed diagonally adjacent to a numbered cell do not contribute to the bulb count. An unnumbered black cell may have any number of light bulbs adjacent to it, or none at all, and not all light bulbs are necessarily clued via black squares.

1						
		0		■	**1**	**0**
					2	
■	**1**					
				0		
1						

"Mindfulness means paying attention in a particular way: on purpose, in the present moment, and non-judgmentally."

Jon Kabat-Zinn

85   Skyscrapers

Place the numbers 1 to 5 into each row and column, one number per square. Each number represents a skyscraper of that many floors.

Arrange the skyscrapers in such a way that the given number outside the grid represents the number of buildings which can be seen from that point, looking only at that number's row or column.

A skyscraper with a lower number of floors cannot hide a higher building, but a one with a higher number of floors always hides any building behind it.

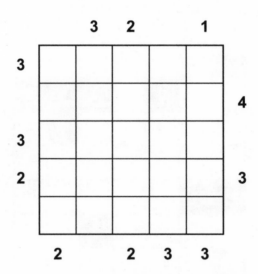

 "Mindfulness is about the present, but I also think it's about being real. Being awake to everything. Feeling like nothing can hurt you if you can look it straight on."

Krista Tippett

Shadow Play

Which of the shadows is that
of the yacht shown here?

A

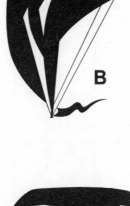

B

C

D

E

F

G

87   Arroword

Solve the clues, then enter each answer in the direction of the arrows, one letter per square.

Deal with / Hairy tropical spider ▼	▼	Wise man, sorcerer ▼	▼	Back of the neck ▼	▼	Of a thing ▼	▼	Division of Ireland
⌐				▼				
Count (3,2)		Hydrogen, for example ▶			Remain		Longings	
⌐					Enclosure for swine / Inform ▶	▼	▼	
Trap made by an arachnid		Couch / Cleanse the entire body ▶		▼				
⌐		▼	Royal person	Make money / Relating to the mail ▶				
Fuel	Make a request ▶	▼	▼			One who looks after a sick relative ▼		
⌐					Queen of heaven and wife of Zeus	▼	Barley used in brewing	
Aroma	Male pronoun / Sound of a dove ▶			Meat cut from the thigh of a pig ▶	▼	▼		
⌐	▼			Long and distinct period of history ▶				
Intestine	Small individual study area in a library ▶							
⌐				Painting, sculpture, etc ▶				

88   Sudoku

Place one of the numbers from 1 to 9 into every empty cell so that each row, each column and each 3x3 block contains all the numbers from 1 to 9.

	5		8		4			7
2	4		1				5	
			6	2			3	1
		2		3	1	6		
	1	3				8	4	
		9	4	6		3		
7	3			1	9			
	6				7		2	4
1			5		6		9	

"Open the window of
your mind. Allow the
fresh air, new lights and
new truths to enter."

Amit Ray

89 Codeword

Every letter in this puzzle has been replaced by a number, the number remaining the same for that letter wherever it occurs. Every letter of the alphabet has been used. Substitute numbers for letters to complete the codeword.

It may help to cross off the letters beneath the grid to keep a track of progress, and to use the reference box showing which numbers have been decoded. Three letters have already been entered into the grid, to help you on your way.

24		16		4	14	16	10	14	24	12	21	20	10	22
12	9	10	14	14		10			20		10		12	
10		14		6	12	25	18	20	1	1	14	21	21	14
4	20	4	9	14		26			19		1		25	
25		25		10		14	12	3	14	18	4	10	20	16
20		18	20	12	17		1		21			14		20
9	12	16		10			21		21		8	12	10	6
10		20		12	2	5	12	21	25	24		4		14
12	7	18	20		5		24			10		15	5	9
16		14			25		25		21	5	21	5		10
13	22	4	10	20	23	25	4	14		6		18		12
	14		14		20			23		16	25	21	20	1
11	12	10	11	25	21 T	5	10	12	21	14		25		12
	18		14		25 I			7		21	14	1	14	21
18	21	12	7	12	24 C	21	25	21	14	18		9		14

A B C D E F G H I J K L M

N O P Q R S T U V W X Y Z

1	2	3	4	5	6	7	8	9	10	11	12	13
14	15	16	17	18	19	20	21 T	22	23	24 C	25 I	26

90   Wordsearch: Authors

Can you find all of the listed words hidden in the grid below?
Words run horizontally, vertically or diagonally, in either a forward or
backward direction.

```
J H S T K N O S C A A S I R P
G E R P N D N A U B P L A T E
O I N S Y E L S G N I K A E A
G R I M M G O L D S M I T H A
T O R E D I D I Q D Y P K R Y
M E L V I L L E V R I L I E E
L C B R O N T E U A U I N I L
A U C N F E E T N W J N S R K
H L R A V O R T P D F G O U C
A A E A F O R K S E A L N A U
Y D N E W F C W S U A U F M B
E S D O A V R C E A A C S U E
E T E A T D A E R L C I O D Y
I I L B T E I D Y P L A E C X
B S L G Y H S W O O H N R N K
```

ARNOLD	DIDEROT	KIPLING
ATKINSON	DU MAURIER	LAHAYE
AUSTEN	EDWARDS	LUCIAN
BRONTE	EVANS	MCCAFFREY
BUCKLEY	GOLDSMITH	MELVILLE
CLEMENS	GRIMM	ORWELL
CRAIS	ISAACSON	PEACOCK
DEFOE	KINGSLEY	RENDELL

91   No Three in Line

Place either O or X into each empty square, so that no three consecutive squares in either a horizontal row or vertical column contain more than two of the same symbol.

There needs to be as many Os as Xs in every row and column.

		X		X	X		
O					O		
X	O		X			O	O
O	O						O
		O	O				
		X	X		X	X	
							O
	X			X			

**"Ultimately, it is only
by mindfully caring for
ourselves that we can
truly and effectively
care for others with
compassion."**

Arnie Kozak

92   Flower Power

Fit the listed words into the grid below (one letter is already in place), then rearrange the letters in the shaded squares to form another word related to the theme of this book.

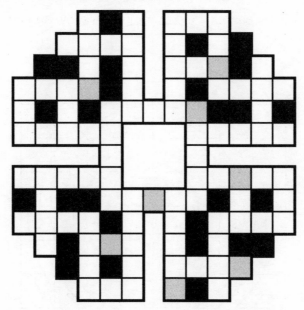

3 letters	4 letters		5 letters	
ACE	ABET	JUMP	ADIEU	DEISM
ANY	ABLE	LAVA	AMBER	DOYEN
ASP	CHAT	MOLE	ANNUL	EASEL
CAP	CUBE	ORAL	APPLE	EPOCH
COD	DARK	PINT	AUGER	LATEX
GNU	JIBE	TOOK	CHOKE	RELAX
OWN				
RIP				

"Enlightenment is the result of the daily practice of mindfulness."

Shinjo Ito

93   Maze

Start at the top and find a path to the middle of the maze.

"Practice isn't the
thing you do once
you're good. It's the
thing you do that
makes you good."

Malcolm Gladwell

94   **Combiku**

Each horizontal row and vertical column should contain five different shapes, and five different numbers.

Every square will contain one number and one shape, and no combination may be repeated anywhere else in the puzzle; so, for instance, if a square contains a 3 and a star, then no other square containing a 3 will also contain a star, and no other square with a star will also contain a 3.

1   **2**   **3**   **4**   **5**

○   ☆   ⬡   ◇   ☐

		1	5	○
1	5	◇		4
☆	1	5	3	
◇				
	2	☐	◇	☆

"The point of power is always in the present moment."

Louise Hay

Every row and column of this grid should contain one each of the letters A, B, C, D, and E.

In addition, each of the five shapes (marked by thicker lines) should also contain one each of the letters A, B, C, D, and E.

Can you complete the grid?

			B	C
			C	
	B			D
			E	A
	A			

"For me mindfulness is like building a house, so the next time the tsunami that is depression comes I'll have a structure in place to resist it."

Ruby Wax

Wordsearch: Floral Clock

Can you find all of the listed words hidden in the grid below?
Words run horizontally, vertically or diagonally, in either a forward or
backward direction.

```
N E S T E N I S T P E R F Y T
A D E A L V C Y N E E U S D M
I I I H C O O B Z D V M I W C
G N S R R Y B N N H G I H H M
N B N K O S H E F Q N N R S I
I U A H R L V I L S I U U P A
D R P A B A J T E I P T H I I
N G A N L M P T V U A E O L R
E H H D X R A A A F H S U U E
T S E S S O M H R Q S S R T V
H C R L U F C C G A I U S R E
Y R B H E J A M R L G E P P H
M E S I L I O M A D D A O I C
E F Q M O K B X B U Y L I T E
S E N E C I O J M J S U T N E
```

COLEUS

ECHEVERIA

EDINBURGH

FORMAL

GRAVEL

HANDS

HERBS

HOURS

LAVENDER

LOBELIA

MCHATTIE

MINUTES

MOSSES

NIAGARA
    PARKS

OXALIS

PANSIES

PRIVET

SEDUM

SENECIO

SHAPING

SLOPE

TENDING

THYME

TULIPS

97   Coin Collecting

In this puzzle, an amateur coin collector has been out with his metal detector, searching for booty. He didn't have time to dig up all the coins he found, so has made a grid map, showing their locations, in the hope that if he loses the map, at least no-one else will understand it... However, he didn't count on YOU coming across the strange grid (as seen here). Will you be able to discover the correct number of coins and their precise locations?

Those squares containing numbers are empty, but where a number appears in a square, it indicates how many coins are located in the squares (up to a maximum of eight) surrounding the numbered one, touching it at any corner or side. There is only one coin in any individual square.

Place a circle into every square containing a coin.

1			2				
	3	3			2		1
					2	2	
2		4	4		2		1
	3					3	
	3	2	4	5			2
2			2				3
		1		2			2

"What the caterpillar calls the end of the world, the master calls a butterfly."

Richard Bach

Sudoku

Place one of the numbers from 1 to 9 into every empty cell so that each row, each column and each 3x3 block contains all the numbers from 1 to 9.

4					6			2
5	6	1				3	7	4
		3		5	1	9		
6					8	5		
	3		7		4		1	
		9	2					3
		4	6	8		2		
3	7	6				8	9	1
8			9					7

"The important thing is this: to be able at any moment to sacrifice what we are for what we could become."

W E B Dubois

99   Criss Cross: Board Games

The words are provided, but can you fit them all into the grid?

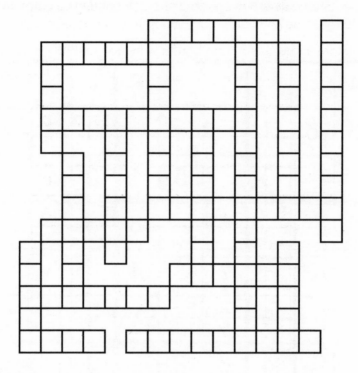

4 letters
LUDO

5 letters
CHESS
HOTEL
SORRY
TSURO

6 letters
BLOKUS
CLUEDO
MEXICA

7 letters
ACQUIRE
PATOLLI
TWISTER

8 letters
IMPERIAL
SCRABBLE

9 letters
MOUSETRAP
OBSESSION
PARCHEESI

10 letters
BATTLESHIP
SQUARE MILE

15 letters
CHINESE
   CHECKERS

Patchwork

Every square should be filled with a letter from A to E, and each heavily outlined set of five squares should contain five different letters. Every row and column must contain two of each letter.

Squares that share a common border may not contain the same letter.

D		C			C		E	A	D
E			A	C	E		A		
		B			B				C
C	B		D	A			C		A
D	A	B		D			B	A	
				B		B		C	
B		A		E					C
			E				E		
	C			E	D				
		D	E						E

"Stop resisting your problems so furiously in your mind. Stop struggling to solve them. If you do that, a great sense of peace followed by a great sense of power will come to you."

Norman Vincent Peale

Slitherlink

Draw a single continuous loop, by connecting the dots. No line may cross the path of another.

The figure inside each set of any four surrounding dots indicates the total number of surrounding lines.

```
.   .   .   .   .   .   .   .   .   .
        3       3   1   2   3   1
.   .   .   .   .   .   .   .   .   .
  2   2   1   3   2
.   .   .   .   .   .   .   .   .   .
  1       1   2   0   2       0
.   .   .   .   .   .   .   .   .   .
  1   2   2   3       3       0
.   .   .   .   .   .   .   .   .   .
  1       2   1   1   0
.   .   .   .   .   .   .   .   .   .
  1       3       1   1       2   3
.   .   .   .   .   .   .   .   .   .
  1   1   2   1       2       0   3
.   .   .   .   .   .   .   .   .   .
          2       1   1   1   3
.   .   .   .   .   .   .   .   .   .
      2                   2
.   .   .   .   .   .   .   .   .   .
```

"In a true you-and-I relationship, we are present mindfully, non-intrusively, the way we are present with things in nature. We do not tell a birch tree it should be more like an elm. We face it with no agenda, only an appreciation that becomes participation: 'I love looking at this birch' becomes 'I am this birch' and then 'I and this birch are opening to a mystery that transcends and holds us both.'"

David Richo

Wordsearch: Eating Out

Can you find all of the listed words hidden in the grid below?
Words run horizontally, vertically or diagonally, in either a forward or
backward direction.

```
G A P Y S K N I R D E X A Y T
D N E S U O H K A E T S T E J
S E I Y R E L T U C N R L E R
A D S P H E R N L P A I L F N
R E R R P A M A T P R Y D F X
E G E H U I Y R R S R E V O C
P B T B X O T U E S R G S C N
P D I T A A C A S U A L E J I
U E A S B R T T S R T O S C K
S P W L T S B S E P E N S C P
S S E A H R D E D E A S A A A
G U P F O M O R C R W R L V N
B A S N O E H C N U L S G L E
S H Y H H O R S D O E U V R E
N E M F I N A I R A T E G E V
```

BARBECUE	GLASSES	SUPPER
BISTRO	HORS D'OEUVRE	SUSHI
COFFEE		SWEET COURSE
COVERS	LUNCHEON	
CUTLERY	NAPKIN	TABLE
DESSERT	PARTY	TAPAS
DINER	RESTAURANT	TIPPING
DRINKS	SEATS	VEGETARIAN
	STEAKHOUSE	WAITER

103   **Arroword**

Solve the clues, then enter each answer in the direction of the arrows, one letter per square.

Lariat ▼	▼	Malicious gossip	Container for a bird	▼	Lay out in a line	Knife that can be fixed to the end of a rifle ▼	▼	Cour-ageous man
Attribute ►		▼	▼					Remedy
Blemish, indication of damage done ►					Con-tinuous portion of a circle ►			▼
Heroic tale ►					Thee ►			
⚑					Wing-shaped		In addition	
Burrowing, rabbit-like animal	Long-necked typically gregarious bird		Sneering look	Stake in poker	▼		▼	
Italian astrono-mer and mathema-tician ►	▼		▼					Minor or small-minded
⚑				At the summit of ►				▼
Pigmented spot on the skin		Elderly person no longer employed (inits)		Pitch		Long fluffy scarf	Charged particle	
Put in order ►		▼		▼	Morsel ►	▼	▼	
⚑			Underway ►					
Light mid-afternoon meal	State of equality ►				Unspeci-fied (object or degree) ►			

104 **Sudoku**

Place one of the numbers from 1 to 9 into every empty cell so that each row, each column and each 3x3 block contains all the numbers from 1 to 9.

					2			4
2					7	8	5	
	7	4	1	3			2	
	9	2			4	5	6	
3				6				7
	6	1	8			3	9	
	3			2	6	4	8	
	4	9	5					1
8			9					

"The only way to make sense out of change is to plunge into it, move with it, and join the dance."

Alan Watts

105   Codeword

Every letter in this puzzle has been replaced by a number, the number remaining the same for that letter wherever it occurs. Every letter of the alphabet has been used. Substitute numbers for letters to complete the codeword.

It may help to cross off the letters beneath the grid to keep a track of progress, and to use the reference box showing which numbers have been decoded. Three letters have already been entered into the grid, to help you on your way.

17	10	5	4	24	4		4	21	3	16	4	6	4	24
10		21		4				3		1		16		17
9	12	9	4	10	17	3		9 **A**		10	4	4	26	21
15		23		18		23	17	10 **M**	19	1		20		5
17	10	10	4	20	21	4		5 **P**		12	17	4	3	4
12			24		4	7	7	17	15	2		17		23
4	25	3	17	21	4		20		9	10	4	12		
24			3		21	8	18	17	24		23			21
		21	26	1	9		17		15	18	7	7	9	6
11		14		21	6	9	26	16	4		17			4
9	25	17	1	10		13		18	26	4	12	21	17	23
22		12		1	3	4	9	12		12		6		26
22	1	12	4	21		12		15	20	4	12	9	24	4
4		4		17		15			10		10			20
21	17	24	4	21	26	4	5		3	9	10	5	18	21

A B C D E F G H I J K L M
N O P Q R S T U V W X Y Z

1	2	3	4	5 **P**	6	7	8	9 **A**	10 **M**	11	12	13
14	15	16	17	18	19	20	21	22	23	24	25	26

106   Pyragram

Every clue in this puzzle is an anagram leading to a single-word solution. Correctly solve the anagram on each level of the pyramid and another word will appear, reading down the central column.

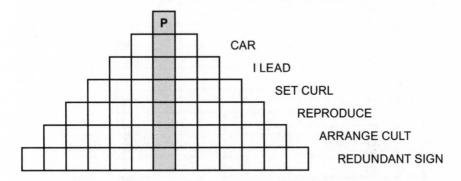

CAR

I LEAD

SET CURL

REPRODUCE

ARRANGE CULT

REDUNDANT SIGN

107   Word Wheel

How many words of three or more letters can you make from those in the wheel, without using plurals, abbreviations or proper nouns?

The central letter must appear once in every word and no letter in a section of the wheel may be used more than once.

There is at least one nine-letter word in the wheel.

Nine-letter word(s):

_____

Criss Cross: Horse Breeds

The words are provided, but can you fit them all into the grid?

5 letters
IOMUD
MOYLE
SHIRE

6 letters
LOSINO
MISAKI
MIYAKO
MORGAN

7 letters
ARABIAN
HACKNEY
SUFFOLK

8 letters
ASTURIAN
BALEARIC
LUSITANO

9 letters
FINNHORSE
GRONINGEN
MONGOLIAN
OLDENBURG

10 letters
BHIRUM PONY

12 letters
CLEVELAND BAY

109   Wordsearch: In the Park

Can you find all of the listed words hidden in the grid below?
Words run horizontally, vertically or diagonally, in either a forward or
backward direction.

```
C  I  S  D  N  U  O  R  O  G  Y  R  R  E  M
B  Y  S  S  R  E  W  O  L  F  U  A  G  Z  D
S  A  A  B  S  U  O  B  E  M  E  N  D  O  D
T  I  R  T  E  S  E  R  A  K  E  O  D  N  G
R  P  G  A  I  N  B  P  N  U  J  L  R  N  W
O  X  B  N  C  Q  G  U  T  L  T  I  I  P  T
P  S  N  H  L  V  K  A  R  V  A  K  T  Q  E
S  E  E  R  T  S  T  K  V  H  L  C  S  K  A
T  S  T  H  E  S  E  T  S  A  S  I  H  D  D
E  E  B  A  S  G  S  E  W  A  E  N  T  B  U
C  T  T  S  W  U  R  N  S  M  L  C  A  P  C
N  S  B  S  E  F  B  F  A  A  V  I  P  O  K
E  T  G  E  A  S  A  Z  K  W  Z  P  R  N  S
F  O  E  E  L  P  O  E  P  E  S  T  O  D  I
D  Z  G  S  L  E  R  R  I  U  Q  S  V  S  L
```

BENCHES	LAKE	SHRUBS
BUSHES	MERRY-GO-ROUND	SPORTS
DOGS		SQUIRRELS
DUCKS	PATHS	STATUE
FENCE	PEOPLE	SWANS
FLOWERS	PICNIC	TENNIS
FRESH AIR	PONDS	TREES
GRASS	ROSES	WALKING
	SEATS	

110   Calcudoku

Each row and column should contain different numbers from 1 to 6.

The numbers placed in a heavily outlined set of squares may be repeated, but must produce the calculation in the top left corner, using the mathematical symbol provided: multiply (x), divide (/), add (+), and subtract (–).

For example, when multiplied, the numbers 4 and 3 total 12:

12x	
4	**3**

18+			3/	120x	
	7+	10+			
24x			4/		4+
	15x		4–		
	6+	1–	150x	48x	

"Spread love everywhere you go. Let no one ever come to you without leaving happier."

Mother Teresa

Bridges

Join the circular islands by drawing horizontal or vertical lines to represent bridges, in such a way that the number of bridges connected to each island must match the number on that island. No bridge may cross another, and no more than two bridges can join any pair of islands.

The finished design will allow you to travel from one island to any other island on the map.

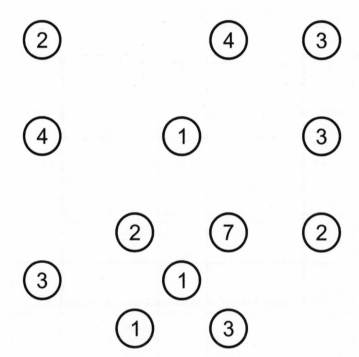

"There is no better means of attainment to the spiritual life than by continually beginning again."

St Francis de Sales

112   Arroword

Solve the clues, then enter each answer in the direction of the arrows, one letter per square.

Making a grab for	Snuggle	Behaves in a particular way	▼	Portico or roofed colonnade	▼	Item of footwear	▼	Remove clips, as from a washing line
	▼	▼						
Umberto ___', author				Sticky stuff		Smooth fabric		Slightly sticky to the touch
Scenery and other properties of a drama (5,3)			▼			▼		▼
		Place where vehicles halt (3,4)			Farm-house cooker	▶		
Of a thing	Sea vessel ▶		▼				Decline	
			Nickname of US president Eisen-hower		Gall ▶		▼	
Dandy	King of the beasts	Poitier, 'To Sir, with Love' actor ▶		▼				
	▼				'Maria', prayer to the Virgin Mary	Artificial covering for a tooth		For each
Bottle with a narrow neck		Drinking vessel ▶			▼	▼		▼
			Jar of glass or porcelain ▶					
Tolerable, indifferent (2-2)		One's eye (coll) ▶						

113 Sudoku

Place one of the numbers from 1 to 9 into every empty cell so that each row, each column and each 3x3 block contains all the numbers from 1 to 9.

	7				4	5	6	
				1	7	2		
8	9	4						1
4			5	3		6		2
		8	6		9	1		
5		9		4	2			7
1						8	2	3
		2	4	5				
	3	6	8				7	

"The passing moment is all that we can be sure of; it is only common sense to extract its utmost value from it."

W. Somerset Maugham

114   Codeword

Every letter in this puzzle has been replaced by a number, the number remaining the same for that letter wherever it occurs. Every letter of the alphabet has been used. Substitute numbers for letters to complete the codeword.

It may help to cross off the letters beneath the grid to keep a track of progress, and to use the reference box showing which numbers have been decoded. Three letters have already been entered into the grid, to help you on your way.

13	23	8	23	16	3	■	17	4	7	4	13	4	8	4
4	■	22	■	25	■	25	■	5	■	14	■	12	■	22
17	4	8	25	13	■	11	12	5	13	11	12	19	23	14
1	■	11	■	25	15	9	■	11	■	23	■	23	■	11
9 L	11 I	3 T	■	12	■	2	23	20	3	22	21	9	23	3
23	■	2	■	23	■	■	12	■	22	■	25	■	17	■
2	18	22	4	13	11	2	7	■	1	4	9	2	4	17
■	22	■	13	■	12	■	4	■	23	■	11	■	11	■
16	4	13	23	2	2	■	12	4	13	13	25	15	9	6
■	24	■	12	■	23	■	16	■	■	4	■	4	■	23
21	23	12	4	9	3	11	23	2	■	17	■	19	23	9
9	■	25	■	11	■	2	■	25	14	23	■	3	■	9
4	14	10	25	16	4	3	23	14	■	24	7	4	24	11
26	■	23	■	11	■	9	■	4	■	11	■	11	■	12
4	9	9	25	3	3	23	14	■	22	12	16	9	25	19

A B C D E F G H I J K L M

N O P Q R S T U V W X Y Z

1	2	3 T	4	5	6	7	8	9 L	10	11 I	12	13
14	15	16	17	18	19	20	21	22	23	24	25	26

Wordsearch: Children

Can you find all of the listed words hidden in the grid below?
Words run horizontally, vertically or diagonally, in either a forward or
backward direction.

```
T N A F N I G N I R P S F F O
M L E F H L P E B A E T F C S
A Y Y T K U A Y L A S S I E H
R O U O P Y N V P O I T C M A
I O N I U E L C S H O R A G V
Y A L I G N M G H T M E N D E
B H A O B I G E T I U A Z D R
V D R N U M A O N O A D M T R
R P E O R P A O N I T G E A D
E Z G S E T R B E E H Y S N U
L B A P H E I D D A L C N B T
D T N E C S E L O D A R R I E
D F E T S A I A N L M W E U T
O R E S T H D E L I N E V U J
T C T T C R E T S G N U O Y A
```

ADOLESCENT	LASSIE	STUDENT
BAIRN	MINOR	TEENAGER
BAMBINO	OFFSPRING	TINY TOT
CHERUB	PROGENY	TODDLER
CHILD	PUPIL	URCHIN
INFANT	RASCAL	YOUNG ONE
JUVENILE	SHAVER	YOUNGSTER
LADDIE	STEPSON	YOUTH

Criss Cross: Affirm

The words are provided, but can you fit them all into the grid?

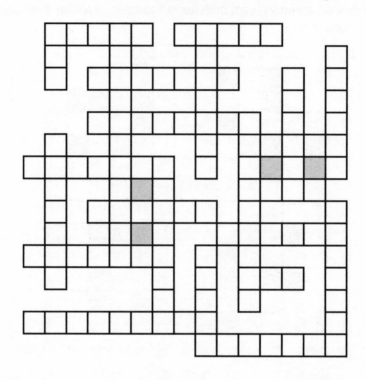

3 letters
SAY
VOW

4 letters
AVER

5 letters
AGREE
STATE
SWEAR
VOUCH

6 letters
ALLEGE
ASSERT
PLEDGE
RATIFY

7 letters
CONFIRM
CONFORM
DECLARE
ENDORSE
PROFESS
PROTEST
TESTIFY

8 letters
MAINTAIN
POSITIVE

9 letters
ESTABLISH
PRONOUNCE

11 letters
CORROBORATE

Flower Power

Fit the listed words into the grid below, then rearrange the letters in the shaded squares to form another word related to the theme of this book.

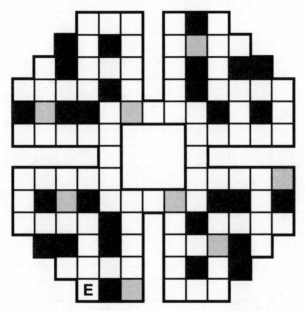

E

3 letters	4 letters		5 letters	
AIL	ABUT	GALE	CHIEF	PEACE
GYM	AMEN	LORD	CRISP	PRESS
LET	AWRY	LYRE	FLOSS	RIGHT
NET	CUBA	TWIN	FLUSH	SCANS
PEW	DIAL	WILL	LEANT	SCRAP
PUN	DIVE	WREN	MOTOR	SKULL
RUM				
WIG				

"Stop, breathe, look around
and embrace the miracle of
each day, the miracle of life."

Jeffrey A White

No Four in Line

Place either O or X into each empty square, so that no four consecutive squares in a straight line in any direction (horizontally, vertically, or diagonally) contain more than three of the same symbol.

X	X			O		O	O	X
X			X			O		O
O						X	O	X
	X						X	
X				O				X
X	X							X
X			X	X	X		X	
	O			X			O	X
X	X		X	X			O	O

"Feelings, whether of
compassion or irritation,
should be welcomed,
recognized, and treated
on an absolutely equal
basis; because both
are ourselves."

Thich Nhat Hanh

119   Pyragram

Every clue in this puzzle is an anagram leading to a single-word solution. Correctly solve the anagram on each level of the pyramid and another word will appear, reading down the central column.

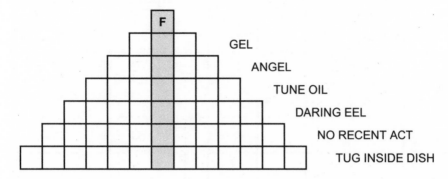

GEL

ANGEL

TUNE OIL

DARING EEL

NO RECENT ACT

TUG INSIDE DISH

120   Word Ladder

Change one letter at a time (but not the position of any letter) to make a new word – and move from the word at the top of the ladder to the word at the bottom using the exact number of rungs provided.

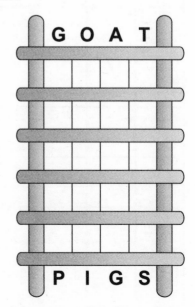

GOAT

PIGS

121   Arroword

Solve the clues, then enter each answer in the direction of the arrows, one letter per square.

Severe shortage of food ▼		Flexible container with a single opening ▼		Fascinated, enthralled	Metal-worker ▼		Fruits of the blackthorn ▼	
Irregular ▶		▼						
Make imperfect ▶				Dried grape	Corrode, as with acid		Tipster	
▶				▼	▼		▼	
Tube of tobacco wrapped in paper	Feeling of sympathy ▶ / Seedcake ingredient							
▶	▼					Golden-yellow songbird with black wings		Bedlinen items
Frenzied / Italian operatic composer	Oust	Sounds of a gun being fired ▶ / Blockhead				▼		▼
▶	▼		▼			Dull, dreary	Wooden shoe	
Yellowing of the skin ▶ / Stitched						▼	▼	
▶			Actor's portrayal of someone ▶					
The sperm whale ▶ / Eye infection								
▶				Implores ▶				

Wordsearch:
Hope

Can you find all of the underlined words from the poem "Hope" by Emily Dickinson? Words run forward or backward, in either a horizontal, vertical, or diagonal direction.

```
B T S E L L I H C E S U N
M A Y S S E H C R E P D A
U E T S G E A R A O N O I
R A I D T N U H S A B A H
C L M R D F I P L S O U L
E E E O W R E H L P N W T
N S R W S S A I T E Q P T
U R T T O W T E V R E D S
T E X R S T E E H K O E E
S H E E L U R E N D U K G
T T M E C B M L T E L S N
O A O R I O Y A W E I A A
P E O R A P U G N N S F R
S F D R M W F L G Y H T T
T U O H T I W S D A F E S
```

Hope is the thing with feathers
That perches in the soul,
And sings the tune without the words,
And never stops at all.

And sweetest in the gale is heard;
And sore must be the storm
That could abash the little bird
That kept so many warm.

I've heard it in the chillest land,
And on the strangest sea;
Yet, never, in extremity,
It asked a crumb of me.

123   Codeword

Every letter in this puzzle has been replaced by a number, the number remaining the same for that letter wherever it occurs. Every letter of the alphabet has been used. Substitute numbers for letters to complete the codeword.

It may help to cross off the letters beneath the grid to keep a track of progress, and to use the reference box showing which numbers have been decoded. Three letters have already been entered into the grid, to help you on your way.

17	25	26	26	3	7		25	17	5	23	20	7	4	23
11		5		25				5		11		25 A		5
23	7	4	5	22	7	16		22		10	25	22 R	7	22
6		24		24		7	9	7	22	21		20 M		22
7	10	15	23	11	20	7		25		15	20	25	24	7
22			6		15	20	17	5	7	16		22		23
7	8	14	7	10	23		3		4	7	14	1		
16			23		23	15	25	22	25		22			10
		14	25	10	7		18		17	3	11	23	14	6
12		25		5	4	22	7	25	3		14			25
5	23	23	7	22		7		13	7	22	1	15	7	22
25		7		2	15	3	3	25		7		21		20
14	11	22	24	15		15		22	15	14	11	23	23	25
1		7		7		2			23		3		14
21	10	22	25	9	3	7	22		10	11	10	7	22	19

A B C D E F G H I J K L M

N O P Q R S T U V W X Y Z

1	2	3	4	5	6	7	8	9	10	11	12	13
14	15	16	17	18	19	20 M	21	22 R	23	24	25 A	26

124   **Sudoku**

Place one of the numbers from 1 to 9 into every empty cell so that each row, each column and each 3x3 block contains all the numbers from 1 to 9.

6		4	3		2	5		
5			6		7	8		
	8			9				1
		1			5		2	6
		7		3		4		
9	4		8			3		
4				7			5	
		8	4		1			2
		9	2		3	7		8

 "It is only possible to live happily-ever-after on a day-to-day basis."

Margaret Wander Bonnano

125   Criss Cross: Better and Better

The words are provided, but can you fit them all into the grid?

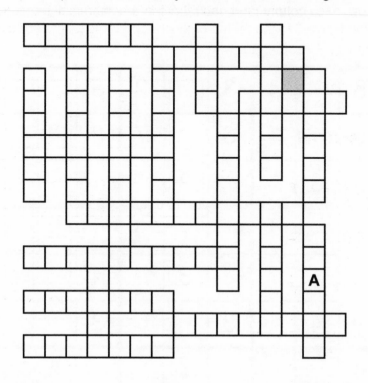

4 letters
WELL

5 letters
FINER
NICER

6 letters
FITTER
HEALED
LARGER
MENDED
NEATER

7 letters
GREATER
REVISED
SMARTER
SOUNDER
SWEETER

8 letters
POLISHED
REFORMED
SUPERIOR

9 letters
A CUT ABOVE
TOUCHED UP

10 letters
PREFERABLE

11 letters
PROGRESSING

126   In Place

Place the listed words horizontally into the grid, so that when read from top left to bottom right, the letters in the shaded squares spell out a word linked to the theme of this book. Some letters are already in place.

ATTUNED

BENEFIT

COMPACT

GREATER

MAXIMUM

SOMEONE

WELFARE

		N				
				M		
		M				
				O		

"Mindfulness requires
that we not over-identify
with thoughts and
feelings so that we are
caught up and swept
away by negativity."

Brené Brown

127

Maze

Start at the top and find a path to the middle of the maze.

"Once you replace
negative thoughts with
positive ones, you'll start
having positive results."

Willie Nelson

128   Wordsearch: Herbal Remedies

Can you find all of the listed words hidden in the grid below?
Words run horizontally, vertically or diagonally, in either a forward or
backward direction.

```
G A R L E A S T R E M O R K O
A W O L L A M H S R A M C R Y
L A R E G N I G H U A U R J E
A L O E V E R A P S N I U A R
N L E G N O G O Y L I S D H D F
G E B U K L A A R K L E E K M
A G V O K N B R C A A S N W O
L M I V R U I O L R M P W N C
U H O N N A L G T I A E A O A
S U L I S M G S I R C T S X C
A B E O E E E E S A F F R O N
T A T H V A N L E N E R A S R
F S M D S A E G L E R R O S Y
E I A E J Y G O L D E N R O D
N L I N E R I E H E P T R I D
```

ALOE VERA	GINGER	ORRIS
BALSAM	GINKGO	PARSLEY
BASIL	GINSENG	ROSEMARY
BORAGE	GOLDENROD	SAFFRON
COMFREY	HEARTSEASE	SENNA
COWSLIP	HEMLOCK	SORREL
GALANGAL	LOVAGE	SUNDEW
GARLIC	MARSH-MALLOW	VIOLET

129   Futoshiki

Fill the grid so that every horizontal row and vertical column contains all the numbers 1 to 7.

Any arrows in the grid always point toward a square that contains a lower number.

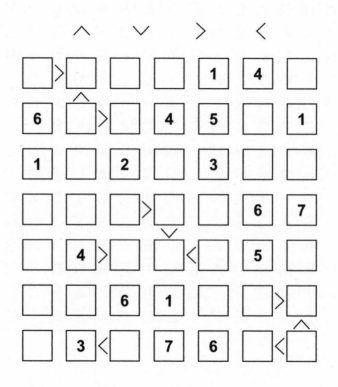

"Wanderer, your footsteps
are the road, and nothing
more; wanderer, there
is no road, the road is
made by walking."

Antonio Machado

Sudoku

Place one of the numbers from 1 to 9 into every empty cell so that each row, each column and each 3x3 block contains all the numbers from 1 to 9.

8	5			7	4			
1		3		8			6	
6		2				9	7	
9			3			1		
	6	1	7		8	3	5	
		4			5			2
	9	7				5		4
	2			3		8		1
			4	9			3	6

"To escape the self-trap, to be sane and decent and awake and whole – that is all that matters."

Vernon Howard

131   Domino Placement

A standard set of 28 dominoes has been laid out as shown. Can you draw in the edges of them all?

The check-box is provided as an aid, so that you can see which dominoes have been located.

3	3	1	4	6	0	1
4	2	2	3	4	3	1
0	0	6	5	6	2	3
1	0	4	4	6	4	0
0	4	2	6	1	6	4
2	2	6	3	3	0	5
5	1	2	0	5	2	5
3	1	6	5	5	1	5

0-0	0-1	0-2	0-3	0-4	0-5	0-6	1-1	1-2	1-3	1-4	1-5	1-6	2-2

2-3	2-4	2-5	2-6	3-3	3-4	3-5	3-6	4-4	4-5	4-6	5-5	5-6	6-6
										✓			

"Mindfulness is awareness
without comment,
without discrimination,
without judgment."

Steven Harrison

Jigsaw

Which four shapes (two black and two white) can be fitted together to form the hummingbird shown here? The pieces may be rotated, but not flipped over.

A

B

C

D

E

F

G

H

I

J

K

L

M

N

133   Criss Cross: In Our Dreams

The words are provided, but can you fit them all into the grid?

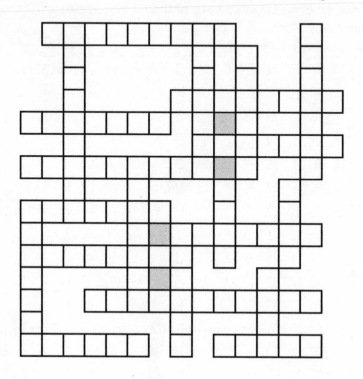

4 letters
FOOD
HOME
WORK

5 letters
SHEEP

6 letters
FAMILY
FLYING
SCHOOL

7 letters
ANIMALS
CASTLES
COFFINS
FALLING
FLOWERS
IRONING
THE PAST
THE WIFE

8 letters
FOOTBALL
SWIMMING

9 letters
CHOCOLATE
HAPPINESS
THE FUTURE

11 letters
GETTING LOST

134 Wordsearch: Train Ride

Can you find all of the listed words hidden in the grid below?
Words run horizontally, vertically or diagonally, in either a forward or
backward direction.

```
Y R E N E C S J M R N W E N D
G A E Y F W I N D O W A L E O
S N A E S I L E J T R E T A F
A O I N C S Y P E C R A S R H
K A T R H E R S A U T G I Y G
A R E U E A E V T D M D H L N
E R K O D T A R K N O H W P S
P I C J U S A T M O R A L I S
F V I L L P R C R C E C J I Z
F A T E E A M S Y O N T G K M
O L E D V B U F F E T N U L T
L H F E R E S E R V A T I O N
W U L U G G E L S L E E P E R
E A S S A L C T S R I F S Z Q
R B E N I G N E L U G G A G E
```

ARRIVAL	JOURNEY	SEATS
BUFFET	LUGGAGE	SIGNALS
CATERING	OFF-PEAK	SLEEPER
CONDUCTOR	RAILS	TICKET
DEPARTURE	RESERVATION	TRAVEL
DOORS	ROUTE	WHEELS
ENGINE	SCENERY	WHISTLE
FIRST CLASS	SCHEDULE	WINDOW

135   Number Link

Working from one square to another, horizontally or vertically (never diagonally), draw single continuous paths to pair up each set of two matching numbers.

No line may cross another, none may travel through any square containing a number, and every square must be visited just once.

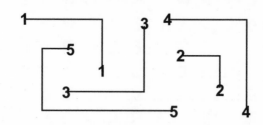

		12	11					8
12		1	10					3
		15		8		16		
1	15			11	2		3	4	
9	10			7			18		
		9				18	6		
7				13				16
				14				4
		5	17			2		6
17	5	13						14

"Passion is energy. Feel the power that comes from focusing on what excites you."

Oprah Winfrey

136   Pyragram

Every clue in this puzzle is an anagram leading to a single-word solution. Correctly solve the anagram on each level of the pyramid and another word will appear, reading down the central column.

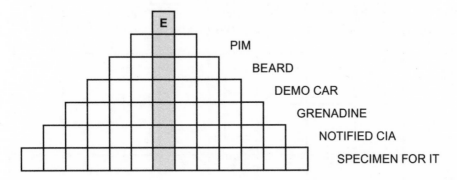

PIM

BEARD

DEMO CAR

GRENADINE

NOTIFIED CIA

SPECIMEN FOR IT

137   Word Wheel

How many words of three or more letters can you make from those in the wheel, without using plurals, abbreviations or proper nouns?

The central letter must appear once in every word and no letter in a section of the wheel may be used more than once.

There is at least one nine-letter word in the wheel.

Nine-letter word(s):

_____

138   Arroword

Solve the clues, then enter each answer in the direction of the arrows, one letter per square.

Make or pass laws	▼	Blood pump	▼	Looks at	Naked	▼	Flesh used as food	▼
⌐								
Platform for a lookout on a mast (5,4)		Idiots		Un-wavering	Following		Young child (coll)	
⌐		▼		▼	▼		▼	
Discernment ▶					Bind by conditions, etc (3,4)		Conse-crates with oil	
Pregnancy	Consume (3,2)		Additional ▶		▼		▼	
⌐	▼							
Com-pletely filled	Latin name of two constella-tions	Paws, trotters, etc		Inflated pride ▶				
⌐	▼	▼					Marry	
Waste product useful as a fertiliser ▶				Have ▶		▼		
⌐				Soaked with a liquid ▶				
Church recesses	Pays heed ▶							

Sudoku

Place one of the numbers from 1 to 9 into every empty cell so that each row, each column and each 3x3 block contains all the numbers from 1 to 9.

		7		9		3		
	1	4			7	9	2	
9		5	6			7		1
			8	3			6	7
4								2
5	7			1	2			
6		9			4	2		8
	8	1	9			5	3	
		3		5		6		

"We cannot live in the past; it is gone. Nor can we live in the future; it is forever beyond our grasp. We can live only in the present."

S.N. Goenka

140   Codeword

Every letter in this puzzle has been replaced by a number, the number remaining the same for that letter wherever it occurs. Every letter of the alphabet has been used. Substitute numbers for letters to complete the codeword.

It may help to cross off the letters beneath the grid to keep a track of progress, and to use the reference box showing which numbers have been decoded. Three letters have already been entered into the grid, to help you on your way.

20		7		13	16	25	10	6	16	10	5	23	18	10
10	5	8	10	20		18			19		13		13	
2		10		7	21 H	5 A	16 M	10	18	10	7	7	18	15
4	21	5	4	13		9			18		18		5	
10		16		3		5	2	26	11	13	10	7	2	10
6		6	10	20	8		21		7			21		1
2	19	19		13			10		4		7	19	24	5
21		18		5	8	21	10	13	7	8		12		3
13	7	18	10		13		8			6		17	11	3
10		10			8		5		16	10	20	11		10
24	19	6	8	20	13	3	21	8		5		16		6
	22		11		22			6		7	10	25	13	5
25	19	6	8	16	5	20	8	10	5	11		13		8
	18		19		8			10		6	5	20	3	10
2	19	11	6	8	10	19	11	7	18	15		3		14

A   B   C   D   E   F   G   H   I   J   K   L   M

N   O   P   Q   R   S   T   U   V   W   X   Y   Z

1	2	3	4	5 A	6	7	8	9	10	11	12	13
14	15	16 M	17	18	19	20	21 H	22	23	24	25	26

141 Wordsearch: Theatrical

Can you find all of the listed words hidden in the grid below?
Words run horizontally, vertically or diagonally, in either a forward or backward direction.

```
C S A T O E R T E R C C A R D
U K U S T I E S L H D A I S T
B C P W C S M R A O R R L E I
E A R L E I M O X U E E E L P
U R O R A A I T W S D S V C A
Z T P O I M D C Y E R S B U R
H C E S J G A E D K O E A E T
X U R T S T G R E A G R N S S
G T T R T Y P I D I N D A H E
U O I U R R J D N D I C H E H
X U E M O N E N V G N M M E C
G T S H B O E E S D N O Y T R
P A C K E R E W E N U R T A O
I N S R S B A C K D R O P E P
A H B L A C K O U T D Y E R S
```

ANCHOR	DECK	PRESET
BACKDROP	DIMMER	PROPERTIES
BEGINNERS	DIRECTOR	RIGGING
BLACKOUT	DRAMA	ROSTRUM
CALL	DRESSER	RUNNING ORDER
CAST	HOUSE	
CLOTH	NOTES	STROBE
CUE SHEET	ORCHESTRA PIT	TRACKS
CUT-OUT		

142   Light Up

Place circles (representing light bulbs) in some of the empty squares, in such a way that no two bulbs shine on each other, until every square of the grid is lit up. A bulb sends rays of light horizontally and vertically, illuminating its entire row and column unless its light is blocked by a black cell.

Some black cells contain numbers, indicating how many light bulbs are in adjacent squares either immediately above, below, to the right, or to the left. Bulbs placed diagonally adjacent to a numbered cell do not contribute to the bulb count. An unnumbered black cell may have any number of light bulbs adjacent to it, or none at all, and not all light bulbs are necessarily clued via black squares.

1						
		1	**1**		**2**	
			1			
■						
				■	**0**	
	2			**2**		

"Through recognizing and realizing the empty essence, instead of being selfish and self-centred, one feels very open and free."

Tsoknyi Rinpoche

143   Flower Power

Fit the listed words into the grid below, then rearrange the letters in the shaded squares to form another word related to the theme of this book.

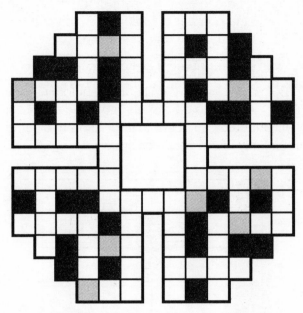

3 letters	4 letters		5 letters	
AFT	FUND	SPIN	ALONG	NOISY
AIR	NUMB	THAT	ANGLE	ORBIT
ASH	ODIN	TIES	BRASS	RABBI
BOY	OMEN	TUNE	EARLY	STAFF
DAB	OPUS	YARN	LLAMA	VERSE
EBB	OVEN	ZERO	LODGE	VIXEN
NUT				
TAR				

"Our vision is more obstructed by what we think we know than by our lack of knowledge."

Kristen Stendahl

144   Skyscrapers

Place the numbers 1 to 6 into each row and column, one number per square. Each number represents a skyscraper of that many floors.

Arrange the skyscrapers in such a way that the given number outside the grid represents the number of buildings which can be seen from that point, looking only at that number's row or column.

A skyscraper with a lower number of floors cannot hide a higher building, but a one with a higher number of floors always hides any building behind it.

	3		3		1	2	
5							
							3
4							1
3							2
1							5
		2		3		5	

"You get peace of mind not by thinking about it or imagining it, but by quietening and relaxing the restless mind."

Remez Sasson

145   **Sudoku**

Place one of the numbers from 1 to 9 into every empty cell so that each row, each column and each 3x3 block contains all the numbers from 1 to 9.

3	5	9		4			8	
				3	8		6	
			9				2	
9		8	1		7	6		2
	1	5				7	3	
4		6	3		2	9		5
	4				1			
	6		8	7				
	9			2		8	5	1

"That the birds of worry and care fly over your head, this you cannot change, but that they build nests in your hair, this you can prevent."

Chinese proverb

Solve the clues, then enter each answer in the direction of the arrows, one letter per square.

Father of Icarus in Greek mythology ▼	▼	Jog	▼	Female child	▼	Ancient Peruvian — Flippantly	▼	In the month preceding the present one (abbr)
►		▼					▼	Fungi used as an agent for raising bread
Sane — Make a mistake ►				Metropolis ► — Plunder				
Australian currency unit ►				▼			Waterside plant	
►			Diffusion of liquid through a porous membrane		Brother of George Gershwin ►		▼	
Took a chair		Lots and lots (coll) ►	▼					
►					Neverthe-less ►			
Popped		Disastrous destiny		Sleep state in which dreaming occurs (inits) ►	▼	Midday		In this place
Commu-nist state of Asia	Quantity of 12 items ► — Alcoholic beverage	▼				▼	Tit for ___, getting even	▼
►	▼			Small particle of dust ►			▼	
Cut of meat — Precious stones ►					Paddle used to move a boat ►			
►				Stake in poker ►				

Wordsearch: Boats

Can you find all of the listed words hidden in the grid below? Words run horizontally, vertically or diagonally, in either a forward or backward direction.

```
C B A N A R A M A T A C E R S
D R Z M E S Y E C H T I H C M
R A U N I B R A Y E M P Y C A
O E K I R N R S R R O T A C C
S Y L E S S E V E O R N E O K
K A Y A K E A S L U O E A R T
B E M E F V R S W E M R F A E
Z P T Y S O G R A E U R O C Y
H C N U A L G C R O E B G L N
H S K I F F S I T G E P A E A
D I F O S E R V D L I S E Y P
R E Y O R T S E D E S B A R M
E U Q R A B R D A I L C E R A
P R A N E D A B C J H E O H S
I W A R E P C U T T E R P W J
```

ARGOSY	DREDGER	SCOW
BARQUE	FERRY	SKIFF
CANOE	KAYAK	SLOOP
CATAMARAN	KETCH	SMACK
CORACLE	LAUNCH	TRAWLER
CRUISER	MINESWEEPER	TRIREME
CUTTER	PADDLE BOAT	VESSEL
DESTROYER	SAMPAN	YACHT

148   Codeword

Every letter in this puzzle has been replaced by a number, the number remaining the same for that letter wherever it occurs. Every letter of the alphabet has been used. Substitute numbers for letters to complete the codeword.

It may help to cross off the letters beneath the grid to keep a track of progress, and to use the reference box showing which numbers have been decoded. Three letters have already been entered into the grid, to help you on your way.

23	11	20	11		18	12	14	15	3		11	25	11	4
12		23	26	11		17		12			23		26	
21	11	1	2		21	16	5	11	21	16		11		11
26			18		15		19			20	16	9	26	23
		10	2	7	3		3	11	13	26			17	
4 R	12 U	21 T		12		4		4		14	11	6	26	8
2		12		10	3	26	11	21	3			11		12
8	26	19	16	21		21		26		15	12	4	26	10
26		16			22	12	11	4	21	16		11		6
10	21	4	2	19		4		17		23		21	4	17
	9			23	26	14	10		24	11	19	26		
15	16	17	19	12			12		26		11			4
23		11		10	21	2	7	5	11		10	16	25	11
11		9			2		11		14	26	21			17
5	26	14	12		15	12	4	18	10		11	1	2	10

A B C D E F G H I J K L M
N O P Q R S T U V W X Y Z

1	2	3	4 R	5	6	7	8	9	10	11	12 U	13
14	15	16	17	18	19	20	21 T	22	23	24	25	26

No Three in Line

Place either O or X into each empty square, so that no three consecutive squares in either a horizontal row or vertical column contain more than two of the same symbol.

There needs to be as many Os as Xs in every row and column.

O			O		O		
		X					
	O	O		O			O
						X	
		O	X	O			X
				O	X		
X		X	O		O		X

"Miracles rest not so much upon faces or voices or healing power coming to us from far off, but on our perceptions being made finer, so that for a moment our eyes can see and our ears can hear what is there about us always."

Willa Cather

150   Criss Cross: Rivers of the USA

The words are provided, but can you fit them all into the grid?

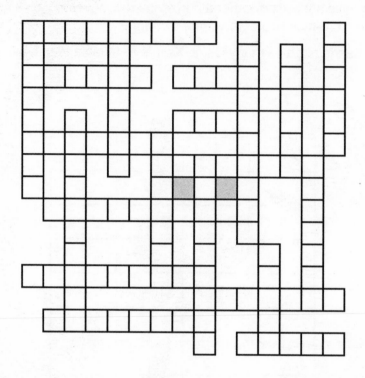

4 letters
GILA
MILK

5 letters
CEDAR
MAPLE
PEARL

6 letters
HUDSON
NOATAK
PUERCO

7 letters
ALAPAHA
ANAHULU
CHARLES
KLAMATH
SCANTIC

8 letters
CHOPTANK
KENTUCKY
KOOTENAI

9 letters
KASKASKIA
OTTER TAIL
PENOBSCOT

10 letters
BLACKSTONE
FARMINGTON
SACRAMENTO

Shadow Play

Which of the shadows is that of the peaceful palm tree shown here?

152   Combiku

Each horizontal row and vertical column should contain five different shapes, and five different numbers.

Every square will contain one number and one shape, and no combination may be repeated anywhere else in the puzzle; so, for instance, if a square contains a 3 and a star, then no other square containing a 3 will also contain a star, and no other square with a star will also contain a 3.

1	2	3	4	5
○	☆	⬡	◇	□

☆		○		
		5	⟨3⟩	1
	□			
	3			⟨2⟩
5	1	⬡	☆	3

"It's not so much that we're afraid of change or so in love with the old ways, but it's that place in between that we fear. It's like being between trapezes."

Marilyn Ferguson

153   Wordsearch: Flower Arranging

Can you find all of the listed words hidden in the grid below?
Words run horizontally, vertically or diagonally, in either a forward or
backward direction.

```
A  R  E  G  N  O  P  S  L  L  E  H  S  H  A
E  C  C  A  H  S  Y  G  B  A  S  K  E  T  R
N  G  O  R  O  E  S  A  N  F  A  S  T  W  E
M  P  R  R  U  I  Z  E  G  I  S  D  E  T  B
P  A  S  E  S  O  R  W  I  E  T  T  F  C  R
W  F  O  O  E  A  S  A  A  R  S  T  E  F  E
Y  I  V  F  P  N  G  T  U  L  R  O  U  M  G
A  X  R  V  L  G  E  E  R  E  P  E  N  C  S
L  S  L  I  A  A  N  R  B  V  E  A  B  L  R
P  C  N  X  N  K  R  O  Y  A  B  B  E  R  Y
S  H  H  O  T  G  U  O  U  R  B  I  M  A  J
I  N  A  Z  B  Q  U  E  L  G  L  N  R  F  P
D  P  R  Y  U  B  A  R  E  F  E  P  D  O  H
S  E  B  E  A  L  I  H  P  O  S  P  Y  G  I
U  R  T  A  F  A  T  R  O  P  P  U  S  K  I
```

BASKET	GERBERA	ROSES
BERRIES	GRAVEL	SHELLS
BOUQUET	GREENERY	SPONGE
CORSAGE	GYPSOPHILA	SPRAY
CUTTING	HOUSE PLANT	STEMS
DISPLAY	NOSEGAY	SUPPORT
FERNS	PEBBLES	WATER
FLORAL FOAM	RIBBONS	WIRING

154   Arroword

Solve the clues, then enter each answer in the direction of the arrows, one letter per square.

Insignia used by the medical profession	▼	Stop sleeping / Body of water (4,3)	As far as (2,2)	▼	Sub-divisions of a play	Inner drives	▼	Region regularly afflicted by monsoons
⌐		▼	▼			▼		Mr Pitt, actor
Held back, retained ▶					Subject to laughter or ridicule ▶			▼
Consumes ▶					Primitive fish ▶			
⌐				Put under a military blockade	Boy's name		Large flightless bird	
Reverse an action	Female relative		Founded ▶	▼	▼		▼	
Central pillar of a circular staircase ▶	▼					Moderately warm		Longs for
⌐			Assemble (3,2) ▶			▼		▼
Through		Conclude	Slang term for diamonds ▶				Former name of Tokyo, Japan	
Waxy part of a bird's beak ▶		▼			Writing tool ▶		▼	
⌐			Move smoothly and effortlessly ▶					
To the full extent (poetically)	Proper and appropriate, fitting ▶				___ and don'ts, rules of behaviour ▶			

Sudoku

Place one of the numbers from 1 to 9 into every empty cell so that each row, each column and each 3x3 block contains all the numbers from 1 to 9.

		7	8		2	5		
9				7				6
	2	5	1		6	7	4	
2			5	8	7			1
	7	4				3	8	
1			2	4	3			7
	1	2	3		8	9	6	
8				2				5
		9	7		4	8		

**"Mindfulness helps you go home
to the present. And every time
you go there and recognize
a condition of happiness that
you have, happiness comes."**

Thich Nhat Hanh

156   Codeword

Every letter in this puzzle has been replaced by a number, the number remaining the same for that letter wherever it occurs. Every letter of the alphabet has been used. Substitute numbers for letters to complete the codeword.

It may help to cross off the letters beneath the grid to keep a track of progress, and to use the reference box showing which numbers have been decoded. Three letters have already been entered into the grid, to help you on your way.

15	17	16	2	9	18		12		15		3	5	25	22
2		2		15		5	25	20	25	19	6			11
14	9	7	11	4	23	2	24		19		19	9	10	17
17		17		2		15		17	19	24	2			18
23	17	7	17	19	19	17	18	7			16	9	11	17
	11				17			11	2	16	9			19
1	5	2	2	23	5	8	24	4	7 T		18	9	13	6
	9		20		9		17		4 H		8		2	
22	7	9	6		7	17	16	3	17 E	19	9	18	11	17
17			24	5	17	18			19				9	
19	8	1	17			13	17	19	22	9	7	8	5	17
19			18	2	22	6		9		11		23		7
8	2	7	9		3		22	26	8	7	7	8	22	4
17			7	2	19	21	25	17		2		2		17
23	8	11	17		6		16		11	19	9	7	17	19

A B C D E F G H I J K L M
N O P Q R S T U V W X Y Z

1	2	3	4 H	5	6	7 T	8	9	10	11	12	13
14	15	16	17 E	18	19	20	21	22	23	24	25	26

157   Pyragram

Every clue in this puzzle is an anagram leading to a single-word solution. Correctly solve the anagram on each level of the pyramid and another word will appear, reading down the central column.

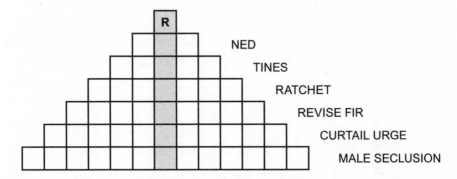

NED

TINES

RATCHET

REVISE FIR

CURTAIL URGE

MALE SECLUSION

158   Word Ladder

Change one letter at a time (but not the position of any letter) to make a new word – and move from the word at the top of the ladder to the word at the bottom using the exact number of rungs provided.

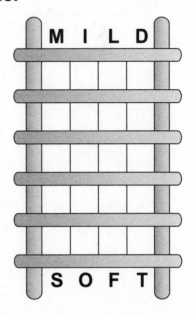

159   Criss Cross: Lights

The words are provided, but can you fit them all into the grid?

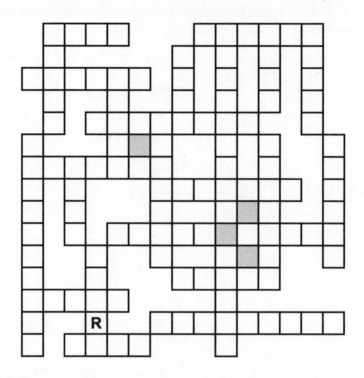

4 letters	MATCH	LANTERN
BEAM	TAPER	VOLTAGE
GLOW	TORCH	
MOON	WATTS	**8 letters**
NEON		DAYBREAK
STAR	**6 letters**	
	AURORA	**9 letters**
5 letters	BRIGHT	REFRACTED
BLAZE	STROBE	SPOTLIGHT
FLAME		
FLARE	**7 letters**	**10 letters**
GLEAM	BONFIRE	FLOODLIGHT
LASER	FIREFLY	

160 Wordsearch: Warm Words

Can you find all of the listed words hidden in the grid below?
Words run horizontally, vertically or diagonally, in either a forward or
backward direction.

```
T Y T I C I R T C E L E F P E
K A L Y N B S E G U V E E A H
E Z I C K S Z U K L T Y V S E
R E U W O U U E N A O D E S A
O T Q Y R M W L R N S W R I T
S R U P R A F E A F Y E I O I
E O I M R A P O I T U J S N N
N P L M Z M D P R E E Z H F G
E I S I E B F I E T S A M I O
Y C U T U S L V A D E I Y R F
J A M G E N I A L T U R R E C
B L M I R U A S N E O P T S O
E B E A D G D O A K Z R L I V
L S R V B F L U S H E D U D E
M E Y E V A W T A E H T S E R
```

BLANKET

COMFORTER

COVER

ELECTRICITY

FEVERISH

FIRESIDE

FLUSHED

GENIAL

GLOWING

HEAT WAVE

HEATING

INSULATE

KEROSENE

LUKEWARM

PASSION

QUILT

RADIATOR

SNUG

SULTRY

SUMMERY

SUNNY

TEMPERATE

TROPICAL

WRAPPED UP

161   **Maze**

Start at the top and find a path to the middle of the maze.

**"No act of kindness,
no matter how small,
is ever wasted."**

Aesop

162   Logi-6

Every row and column of this grid should contain one each of the letters A, B, C, D, E, and F.

In addition, each of the six shapes (marked by thicker lines) should also contain one each of the letters A, B, C, D, E, and F.

Can you complete the grid?

				D	E
	F				C
		E	A		
				F	
	E	C	D	A	

"When we raise ourselves through meditation to what unites us with the spirit, we quicken something within us that is eternal and unlimited by birth and death. Once we have experienced this eternal part in us, we can no longer doubt its existence. Meditation is thus the way to knowing and beholding the eternal, indestructible, essential centre of our being."

Rudolf Steiner

163   Coin Collecting

In this puzzle, an amateur coin collector has been out with his metal detector, searching for booty. He didn't have time to dig up all the coins he found, so has made a grid map, showing their locations, in the hope that if he loses the map, at least no-one else will understand it... However, he didn't count on YOU coming across the strange grid (as seen here). Will you be able to discover the correct number of coins and their precise locations?

Those squares containing numbers are empty, but where a number appears in a square, it indicates how many coins are located in the squares (up to a maximum of eight) surrounding the numbered one, touching it at any corner or side. There is only one coin in any individual square.

Place a circle into every square containing a coin.

1	2			3			1	1
	3				4		3	
2		3		5				2
	2	3		4				
		4			4		3	
						2		
3			3	4			2	
2				3				2
		2	3		4		3	

"Positive energy is attracted to positive energy."

Deborah Day

Sudoku

Place one of the numbers from 1 to 9 into every empty cell so that each row, each column and each 3x3 block contains all the numbers from 1 to 9.

				5	2	3		9
5	1					2	7	
6				9		8	4	
	2		7			6		
3	8		4		1		9	7
		5			9		8	
	9	8		4				3
	6	3					5	1
7		4	2	1				

"Life is ten percent what happens to you and ninety percent how you respond to it."

Charles Swindoll

165   Patchwork

Every square should be filled with a letter from A to E, and each heavily outlined set of five squares should contain five different letters. Every row and column must contain two of each letter.

Squares that share a common border may not contain the same letter.

		D			D	B		B	A
	E		D	A					
	D			E	C				
A			A	B					
	A				B		E		B
	C		A			E	D		
E		C							
C		D			D		B	C	
		E			E				D
	B	E						D	C

"Truth is a deep kindness that teaches us to be content in our everyday life and share with the people the same happiness."

Khalil Gibran

166   Jigsaw

Which four shapes (two black and two white) can be fitted together to form the Buddha can shown here? The pieces may be rotated, but not flipped over.

A

B

C

D

E

F

G

H

I

J

K

L

M

N

167   Criss Cross: Types of Literature

The words are provided, but can you fit them all into the grid?

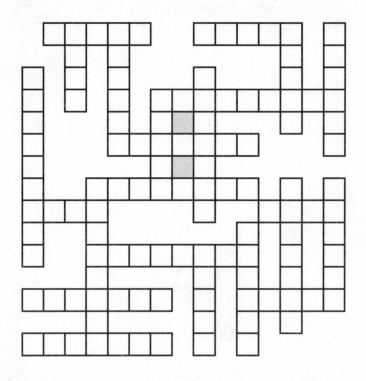

4 letters
EPIC
PULP
SAGA

5 letters
CRIME
ESSAY
NOVEL
ROMAN
TRIAD
VERSE

6 letters
COMEDY
PARODY
SATIRE
THESIS

7 letters
EPISTLE
FANTASY
FICTION
POLEMIC
TRAGEDY

8 letters
ALLEGORY
APOLOGUE
LIBRETTO

9 letters
BIOGRAPHY
CHILDREN'S

168   Reflections

Which of the designs below is an exact horizontal (left to right) mirror image of the design to the right?

1

2

3

4

5

6

7

8

Solutions

1

2

P	A	P	K	A	O	P	A	P	A	T	B	W	D	E
U	U	C	L	J	J	S	C	N	P	E	N	U	M	G
I	H	V	L	H	N	A	W	I	A	T	C	I	A	I
T	K	S	E	V	L	A	L	L	G	I	D	O	L	G
A	P	E	N	R	H	Y	N	A	E	S	R	E	D	F
M	V	A	N	O	T	B	P	H	U	A	E	D	E	R
I	S	R	E	J	H	A	E	K	I	H	A	M	N	Q
T	A	I	R	U	A	S	S	A	N	E	C	K	E	R
I	H	R	L	A	B	O	T	S	I	R	C	N	A	S
R	O	E	V	L	K	E	I	S	R	I	A	U	Z	I
I	W	T	J	X	A	D	F	A	R	I	P	N	H	V
K	L	S	C	N	H	W	T	H	A	W	A	I	I	R
X	A	A	W	E	N	C	A	S	W	S	N	V	G	A
B	N	E	W	C	A	L	E	D	O	N	I	A	H	J
B	D	S	M	U	R	U	R	O	A	V	U	K	G	W

3

	C		B			S		
	U	G	A	N	D	A		B
H	E	R	R		E	L	S	E
		A	B	U	T	T	E	D
A	L	P	S		O		R	
		P		C	U	P	P	A
	S	A	L	A	R	I	E	D
	U		N		E	N	D	
C	R	A	V	A	T		T	
E	W	E	S		R	I	B	
	E	N	T	W	I	N	E	
V	I	S	T	A		P	E	G

4

9	8	1	6	5	3	4	7	2
6	2	5	9	4	7	8	3	1
3	4	7	8	2	1	9	5	6
7	5	9	2	1	4	6	8	3
1	3	4	5	8	6	2	9	7
8	6	2	3	7	9	5	1	4
2	1	6	7	9	5	3	4	8
4	9	8	1	3	2	7	6	5
5	7	3	4	6	8	1	2	9

5

D	I	S	M	I	S	S		Q	U	A	G	G	A
E		C		D		L	I	E	U		T		D
L	E	A	V	E		U		I		T	O		E
T		L		N	O	R	M		N	A	P	K	I	N
A	L	E	R	T		P	E	L	T		E		O
	O		I		N		E		Y		I
A	T	T	I	C		J	U	S	T	I	F	I	E	D
S		A		A		A		I		N		N		A
S	U	N	F	L	O	W	E	R		V	I	G	I	L
E		K		U		A		I		I		N
S		E		T	E	S	T		S	M	O	K	E
S	H	R	I	M	P		Y	E	T	I		X		V
I			D		O		P		B	A	I	Z	E
N			O		S	A	M	E		L		D		R
G	I	M	L	E	T			E	L	E	M	E	N	T

6

			5	4				
		6	6	2	4			
		0	2	2	5			
	3	5	1	1	2	3	3	3
0	6	4	0	5	6	1	4	4	3
1	3	5	3	2	0	0	2	2	4
	1	1	0	6	2	5	1	4
		5	6	4	5			
		1	6	6	0			
			0	3				

Solutions

7

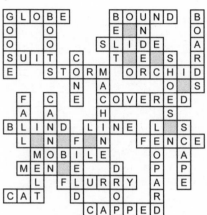

8

9

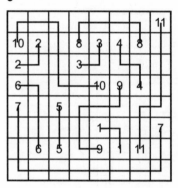

10

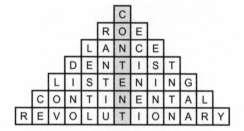

11

The nine-letter word is:
RECEPTIVE

12

	C		B			K		L
R	E	C	O	N	C	I	L	E
	L		X		W		A	
R	E	C	E	S	S	I	O	N
	B	A	S	I	L		P	
		R		N	O	T	E	D
B	A	T			E	U	R	O
	B		A		R	A	Y	
B	A	P	T	I	S	M		E
	T	E	E	M		O	W	N
D	E	N		A	L	I	E	N
		T	O	M		L	E	E

13

8	7	2	5	9	4	3	6	1
3	9	4	1	6	7	5	2	8
1	6	5	2	3	8	7	4	9
4	5	8	9	2	3	1	7	6
2	3	6	7	1	5	8	9	4
9	1	7	8	4	6	2	3	5
7	2	9	4	5	1	6	8	3
5	4	3	6	8	2	9	1	7
6	8	1	3	7	9	4	5	2

Solutions

14

15

16

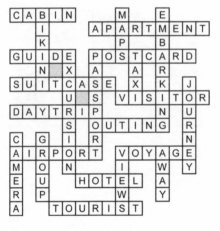

17

Answer: PEACEFUL

18

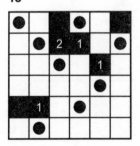

19

8	7	1	5	2	9	6	4	3
4	9	6	1	3	8	7	5	2
3	5	2	7	6	4	1	8	9
5	2	4	3	8	1	9	6	7
1	3	8	6	9	7	4	2	5
7	6	9	4	5	2	8	3	1
9	1	3	8	4	5	2	7	6
6	4	7	2	1	3	5	9	8
2	8	5	9	7	6	3	1	4

Solutions

20

```
      L     K
P U N Y   T I N E
  P E R V A D E
  O B I   B L E W
K N U C K L E   O
  L       E R G O
S C A B   A   E
  H   A B U S E R
C O B R A   T   E
  K   I N L A W S
M E N U   A L O E
  R   M O M E N T
```

21

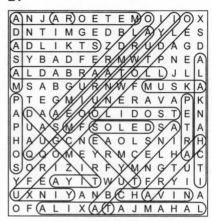

22

23

J I B D

24

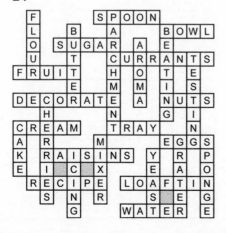

25

26

LAKE - make - male - pale - pole -
poll - POOL
(Other solutions are possible)

Solutions

27

5	1	2	4	3
4	3	1	2	5
2	5	3	1	4
3	2	4	5	1
1	4	5	3	2

28

29

O	O	X	O	X	O	X	X
O	O	X	O	X	O	X	X
X	X	O	X	O	X	O	O
O	O	X	X	O	X	X	O
X	X	O	O	X	O	O	X
O	O	X	O	X	O	X	X
X	X	O	X	O	X	O	O
X	X	O	X	O	X	O	O

30

5	6	7	4	3	2	1	9	8
3	1	2	9	7	8	4	5	6
9	4	8	1	6	5	3	2	7
6	9	5	3	8	7	2	1	4
1	8	3	6	2	4	5	7	9
2	7	4	5	1	9	8	6	3
8	5	1	7	4	6	9	3	2
4	3	6	2	9	1	7	8	5
7	2	9	8	5	3	6	4	1

31

☆3	⬡2	◇4	⬡1
○4	☆1	⬡3	⬡2
◇2	⬡3	○1	☆4
⬡1	◇4	☆2	○3

32

D

Solutions

33
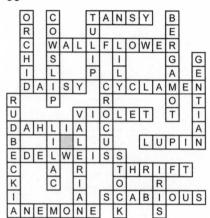

34
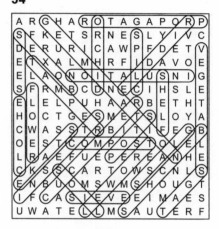

35

36

D	A	C	E	B
B	C	D	A	E
A	E	B	C	D
E	B	A	D	C
C	D	E	B	A

37

		S		A		N		M
A	M	A	S	S		E	K	E
		R		I	M	P	E	L
I	V	I	E	D		O	N	E
		I		S	E	C	T	E
G	A	W	P		H	I	T	
		I		R	I	S	E	S
P	O	S	S	E		M	A	N
	P	E	C	A	N			E
C	I	G	A	R	E	T	T	E
	N	U	N		W	H	I	Z
K	E	Y	S		T	Y	P	E

38

4	9	5	2	1	7	3	6	8
7	2	6	8	9	3	5	4	1
8	3	1	5	4	6	2	7	9
3	8	7	6	2	4	1	9	5
1	6	9	7	8	5	4	3	2
2	5	4	9	3	1	7	8	6
9	4	2	3	5	8	6	1	7
5	7	3	1	6	9	8	2	4
6	1	8	4	7	2	9	5	3

Solutions

39

S	E	X	U	A	L		T	A	I	L	B	A	C	K
K		Y		N			F		O	R		E		E
I	L	L	E	G	A	L		F		R	A	D	O	N
P		E		E		I	N	A	N	E		E		N
J	U	M	B	L	E	D		I		L	A	N	C	E
A		I		C	O	A	R	S	E		C		L
C	L	I	N	C	H		D		T	I	D	Y		
K		G		O	X	I	D	E		I				B
	J	O	K	E		E		R	A	V	A	G	E
Q		A		A	D	D	U	C	E		A		F
U	P	S	E	T		A		Y	O	U	N	G	E	R
A		M		Y	A	W	N	S		S		R		I
I	V	I	E	D		D		T	R	A	P	E	Z	E
N		N		I		L			G		E			N
T	R	E	N	D	I	E	R		V	E	N	T	E	D

40

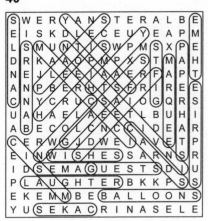

41

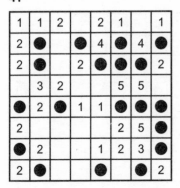

42

Answer: SIMPLICITY

43

B	A	D	A	C	B	D	C
A	C	B	D	A	C	B	D
C	D	A	B	C	D	A	B
D	B	D	C	B	A	C	A
B	A	C	B	D	C	A	D
A	D	B	C	A	D	B	C
D	C	A	D	B	A	C	B
C	B	C	A	D	B	D	A

44

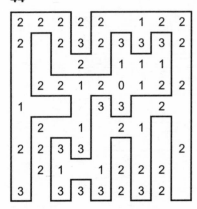

Solutions

45

```
    L   A S
O U T E R W E A R
  N H S   O   L
  R E S T L E S S
A I M   O   R A W
  P   R O A R   E
M E S H     O W E
      U N W R A P
S C U B A     P
  H   A B S E I L
B E A R   A N T I
  F   B A N D I T
```

46

47

```
T R E N C H   V A S T N E S S
R   L   I   Y   T   R   X   U
E J E C T   O U T F O X I N G
E   G   I N K   I   L   S   A
T E A   Z   E S C A L A T O R
O   N   E   E   P   M   N
P A T E N T E D   R A B B I T
  D   N   E   U   O   E   O
W O O D E N   C O N F R O N T
  R   O   E   E   O   V   R
S N O W S T O R M   U   E Y E
Q   A   C   F   O W N   R   A
U N K N O T T E D   D R E A D
I   E   W   E   E   E   A   L
B U N G L I N G   W R I T H E
```

48

5	4	7	6	3	2	9	8	1
2	1	8	9	7	5	6	4	3
9	6	3	1	4	8	7	2	5
8	3	1	7	6	9	4	5	2
6	5	2	3	8	4	1	9	7
4	7	9	2	5	1	8	3	6
7	9	5	8	2	6	3	1	4
3	8	4	5	1	7	2	6	9
1	2	6	4	9	3	5	7	8

49

```
  W     P     L A M P
W A S H I N G     R E S T
  R     L     M   A   N
  M     L U L L A B Y   O
B A T H O     T   E   O
E   H   W     T   R   Z
D         U N D R E S S E D
    C     I   E   L
    D O Z I N G   S H E E T S
R   M     H   S   E       N
E   F   C O T     E       O
L   O   O   G     P       R
A L A R M C L O C K       I
X   T   O   W             N
      Y A W N     S N U G
```

50

4	1	2	3	6	5
6	3	5	2	1	4
5	4	3	6	2	1
3	6	1	5	4	2
1	2	6	4	5	3
2	5	4	1	3	6

Solutions

51

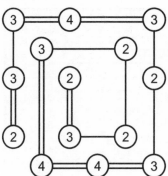

52

53

	Q		A		P		I	
G	U	A	R	D	I	A	N	
	I	C	E		P	S	S	T
	S	H	A	D	E	S		U
A	L	E		A		E	L	M
	I		S	Y	S	T	E	M
G	N	A	T	S		S	A	Y
	G		R		A		F	
		B	A	T	C	H		B
B	R	A	N		T	O	F	U
	O	R	G	Y		B	O	G
T	W	E	E		T	O	G	S

54

9	5	8	1	6	2	4	7	3
1	2	4	3	9	7	6	8	5
3	6	7	5	4	8	1	9	2
4	1	6	2	8	5	9	3	7
7	9	5	6	1	3	2	4	8
2	8	3	9	7	4	5	6	1
8	4	1	7	2	9	3	5	6
6	3	9	8	5	1	7	2	4
5	7	2	4	3	6	8	1	9

55

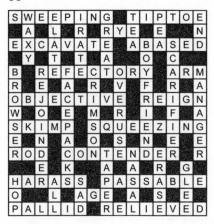

56

Solutions

57

58

59

O	X	X	O	X	O	O	O	X
X	O	O	O	X	X	O	O	O
X	X	O	X	O	X	O	O	X
O	X	X	X	O	O	X	X	X
X	O	O	O	X	O	X	O	X
X	O	O	X	O	O	X	O	O
O	X	X	X	O	X	O	X	X
O	O	X	X	X	O	O	X	X
X	O	X	O	X	O	X	X	X

60

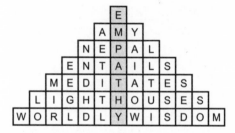

61

The nine-letter word is:
EASYGOING

62

4	3	6	5	2	1
5	6	2	4	1	3
1	5	3	2	6	4
6	4	5	1	3	2
2	1	4	3	5	6
3	2	1	6	4	5

63

3	9	8	1	4	7	2	5	6
5	1	2	6	9	3	7	8	4
4	6	7	5	8	2	3	1	9
2	7	5	9	3	4	8	6	1
8	3	9	2	1	6	5	4	7
1	4	6	8	7	5	9	3	2
7	5	1	3	6	9	4	2	8
6	2	4	7	5	8	1	9	3
9	8	3	4	2	1	6	7	5

Solutions

64

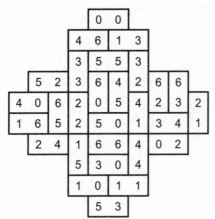

65

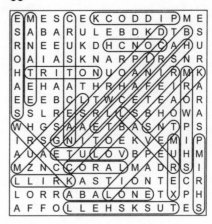

66

67

Answer: GROWTH

68

69

C	R	U	M	B	L	E
W	O	R	K	B	O	X
A	D	M	I	R	A	L
P	E	R	F	E	C	T
H	A	M	M	O	C	K
G	A	L	L	E	R	Y
S	C	A	R	L	E	T

Solutions

70

	R			B	O	W		
	E	W	E	R		E	E	K
	D	O	T	A	R	D		E
B	O	L	A			D	A	B
		F	L	O	R	I	D	A
		R		V		N	I	B
S	C	A	V	E	N	G	E	
	E	M	I	R		M	U	M
	L		S	H	I	A		O
O	L	D	I	E		R	A	N
	A		O	R	A	C	L	E
B	R	I	N	E		H	A	Y

71

72

F	L	Y	I	N	G		A		Y		B	O	Y	S
L		O		E		O	R	M	O	L	U			Y
U	N	D	E	R	C	U	T		G		B	E	A	R
F		E		V		Z		I	A	M	B			I
F	A	L	S	E	H	O	O	D			L	A	W	N
	V			O			O	G	R	E				G
R	A	M	S	H	A	C	K	L	E		G	A	T	E
	I		E		X		I	N		U		U		
P	L	U	M		E	M	P	L	O	Y	M	E	N	T
I			A	W	R	Y			M					I
Q	U	I	P			T	O	L	E	R	A	N	C	E
U		H	U	S	H		I		U		O			N
A	L	T	O		I		J	A	I	L	B	I	R	D
N		R	A	T	H	E	R		E		S			E
T	A	K	E		E	T		F	R	I	E	N	D	

73

2	8	1	7	5	3	4	9	6
5	9	3	4	6	8	7	1	2
7	6	4	2	9	1	8	3	5
8	7	5	9	1	2	6	4	3
3	4	6	5	8	7	9	2	1
1	2	9	3	4	6	5	7	8
4	1	8	6	2	9	3	5	7
9	3	2	8	7	5	1	6	4
6	5	7	1	3	4	2	8	9

74

B	E	S	T	M	A	N			V		T		
U		M		L			T	I	A	R	A		
T		I		L				C		A		A	
T		L		C	A	M	E	R	A		I		I
R	O	S	E	S		R			R	I	N	G	S
N		S		B			T						L
H			E			S	E	R	V	I	C	E	
C	O	N	F	E	T	T	I		L			E	
	L		R		R		E		B		L		
C	E	R	E	M	O	N	Y		G	A	R	T	E	R
A			E		T			R		I		B	
R			S		H	U	S	B	A	N	D	R	
S		W	I	F	E			M		E		A	
		A		D	R	E	S	S				T	
V	O	W	S					P	A	G	E	S	

75

					C						
				T	H	E					
			T	E	A	C	H				
		I	M	P	R	E	S	S			
	C	O	N	T	I	N	U	A	L		
	C	O	N	D	I	T	I	O	N	E	R
M	O	T	O	R	C	Y	C	L	I	S	T	S

76

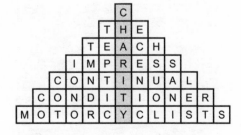

DISH - dash - bash - bass - boss -
bows - BOWL
(Other solutions are possible)

Solutions

77

78

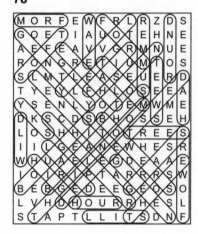

79

	P		A		B		L	
P	R	E	S	T	I	G	E	
	O	B	I		A	R	T	S
	C	O	A	R	S	E		C
K	E	N		A		E	A	R
	E		V	I	E	N	N	A
A	D	D	E	D		S	O	P
	S		N		B		N	
		O	I	L	E	D		R
B	O	B	S		D	A	T	A
W	O	O	D			D	O	G
B	E	E	N		D	O	E	S

80

4	6	1	8	9	7	5	2	3
2	7	8	5	3	4	9	1	6
9	3	5	1	6	2	8	4	7
6	9	3	4	2	1	7	5	8
5	8	2	6	7	9	1	3	4
1	4	7	3	5	8	6	9	2
8	5	4	2	1	6	3	7	9
3	2	9	7	8	5	4	6	1
7	1	6	9	4	3	2	8	5

81

S	E	N	S	I	T	I	V	E		E		C		A
H			O		R		E		A	P	P	L	E	S
A	D	J	U	T	A	N	T	S		I		A		P
K			T		N			C	A	T	A	R	R	H
E	X	C	H	E	Q	U	E	R		O		I		Y
N		E		U			E	L	M		O		X
	F	O	R	C	I	B	L	E		E	N	N	U	I
E		L		L		Y		S		O				A
P	O	L	Y	P		P	E	D	A	N	T	I	C	
I		O		E	R	A		R		O				O
L		Z		R		W	I	N	D	P	R	O	O	F
E	X	E	C	U	T	E		O		I				F
P		N		S		R	A	I	N	C	O	A	T	S
S	I	G	N	A	L		I		I		U			E
Y		E		L		B	L	A	C	K	S	P	O	T

82

5

178

Solutions

83

```
  M A P L E           H
L   I       R   D E A L   A
A   N       R E     Z     S
R O S E W O O D   B E E C H
C   I       W     L   H
H   S Y C A M O R E   Y E W
    A   K       O         S
    N   E       D   B     T
M   A   E       J   A     N
A L D E R         A
H   A     E U C A L Y P T U S
O   R   O   N     S O     T
G R A N A D I L L A   P     T
A   C   K     P     O L I V E
N         E L M       A     A
Y   B R I A R     F I R     K
```

84

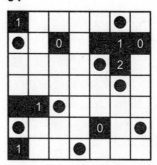

85

2	1	4	3	5
5	4	3	1	2
1	3	2	5	4
3	2	5	4	1
4	5	1	2	3

86

C

87

```
  H   M   I   U
T A R A N T U L A
  N   G A S   S
A D D U P   S T Y
  L   S E T T E E
W E B     E A R N
    A P P L Y   S
P E T R O L   C
    H I S   H A M
S C E N T   E R A
    O   C A R R E L
B O W E L   A R T
```

88

3	5	1	8	9	4	2	6	7
2	4	6	1	7	3	9	5	8
8	9	7	6	2	5	4	3	1
4	8	2	9	3	1	6	7	5
6	1	3	7	5	2	8	4	9
5	7	9	4	6	8	3	1	2
7	3	4	2	1	9	5	8	6
9	6	5	3	8	7	1	2	4
1	2	8	5	4	6	7	9	3

Solutions

89

90

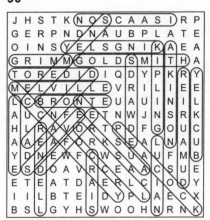

91

O	O	X	O	X	X	O	X
O	X	O	O	X	O	X	X
X	O	X	X	O	X	O	O
O	O	X	X	O	X	X	O
X	X	O	O	X	O	O	X
O	O	X	X	O	X	X	O
X	X	O	O	X	O	O	X
X	X	O	O	X	O	O	X

92

Answer: STRENGTH

93

94

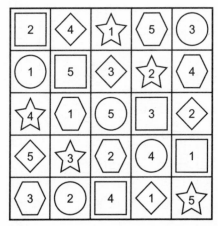

Solutions

95

D	E	A	B	C
A	D	B	C	E
E	B	C	A	D
B	C	D	E	A
C	A	E	D	B

96

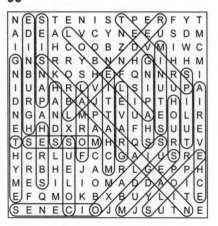

97

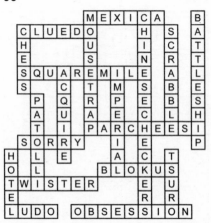

98

4	9	8	3	7	6	1	5	2
5	6	1	8	2	9	3	7	4
7	2	3	4	5	1	9	8	6
6	4	7	1	3	8	5	2	9
2	3	5	7	9	4	6	1	8
1	8	9	2	6	5	7	4	3
9	1	4	6	8	7	2	3	5
3	7	6	5	4	2	8	9	1
8	5	2	9	1	3	4	6	7

99

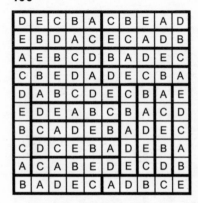

100

D	E	C	B	A	C	B	E	A	D
E	B	D	A	C	E	C	A	D	B
A	E	B	C	D	B	A	D	E	C
C	B	E	D	A	D	E	C	B	A
D	A	B	C	D	E	C	B	A	E
E	D	E	A	B	C	B	A	C	D
B	C	A	D	E	B	A	D	E	C
C	D	C	E	B	A	D	E	B	A
A	C	A	B	E	D	E	C	D	B
B	A	D	E	C	A	D	B	C	E

Solutions

101

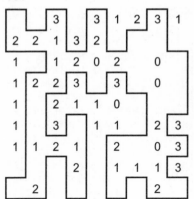

102

103

	L		A		H	
	A	S	C	R	I	B	E
	S	C	A	R		A	R	C
	S	A	G	A		Y	O	U
C	O	N	E	Y		O		R
	D		A	N	T	E
G	A	L	I	L	E	O
M	O	L	E		A	T	O	P
O		E	R			E
S	O	R	T		B	I	T
T	E	A		A	F	O	O	T
	P	A	R		A	N	Y

104

9	8	3	6	5	2	7	1	4
2	1	6	4	9	7	8	5	3
5	7	4	1	3	8	9	2	6
7	9	2	3	1	4	5	6	8
3	5	8	2	6	9	1	4	7
4	6	1	8	7	5	3	9	2
1	3	5	7	2	6	4	8	9
6	4	9	5	8	3	2	7	1
8	2	7	9	4	1	6	3	5

105

106

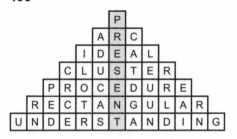

107

The nine-letter word is:
WONDERFUL

Solutions

108

```
  S U F F O L K
S       I         M O Y L E
H A C K N E Y     O     O
I         N       O     S
R         H   M O N G O L I A N
E         O       A     N
  B H I R U M P O N Y   O
  A       S       L           M
C L E V E L A N D B A Y       I
  E             E     R   M   Y
  A S T U R I A N     A   I   A
  R             B     B   S   K
  I O M U D   L U S I T A N O
  C             R     A   K
    G R O N I N G E N         I
```

109

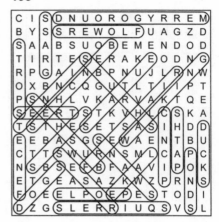

110

5	6	1	3	2	4
6	2	4	1	3	5
2	5	6	4	1	3
4	3	5	2	6	1
3	1	2	5	4	6
1	4	3	6	5	2

111

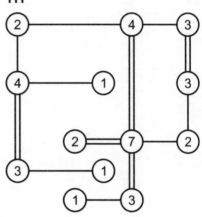

112

```
        S     S     U
S N A T C H I N G
    E C O     O     P
    S T A G E S E T
I T S     O     A G A
    L     B O A T     C
B E A U       I R K
        S I D N E Y
F L A S K       F
    I     T E A C U P
S O S O     V A S E
    N     P E E P E R
```

113

2	7	1	3	8	4	5	6	9
6	5	3	9	1	7	2	4	8
8	9	4	2	6	5	7	3	1
4	1	7	5	3	8	6	9	2
3	2	8	6	7	9	1	5	4
5	6	9	1	4	2	3	8	7
1	4	5	7	9	6	8	2	3
7	8	2	4	5	3	9	1	6
9	3	6	8	2	1	4	7	5

Solutions

114

R	E	J	E	C	T		M	A	H	A	R	A	J	A
A		U		O		O		F		D		N		U
M	A	J	O	R		I	N	F	R	I	N	G	E	D
B		I		O	W	L		I		E		E		I
L	I	T		N		S	E	X	T	U	P	L	E	T
E		S		E		N		U		O		M		
S	Q	U	A	R	I	S	H		B	A	L	S	A	M
	U		R		N		A		E		I		I	
C	A	R	E	S	S		N	A	R	R	O	W	L	Y
	K		N		E		C		A		A		E	
P	E	N	A	L	T	I	E	S		M		G	E	L
L		O		I		S		O	D	E		T		L
A	D	V	O	C	A	T	E	D		K	H	A	K	I
Z		E		I		L		A		I		I		N
A	L	L	O	T	T	E	D		U	N	C	L	O	G

115

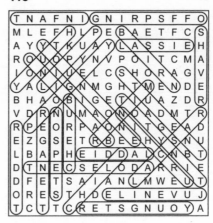

116

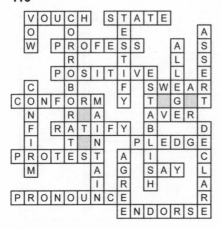

117

Answer: ALTRUISM

118

X	X	O	X	O	X	O	O	X
X	X	O	X	O	O	O	X	O
O	O	O	X	X	O	X	O	X
O	X	X	O	X	O	X	X	O
X	O	O	X	O	X	O	O	X
X	O	X	O	X	O	X	O	X
X	O	O	X	X	O	X	O	X
O	O	X	O	X	O	X	O	X
X	X	O	X	X	O	X	O	O

119

120

GOAT - boat - beat - peat - peas -
pegs - PIGS
(Other solutions are possible)

Solutions

121

	F	E			S		S	
	A	B	N	O	R	M	A	L
	M	A	R		I		O	
C	I	G	A	R	E	T	T	E
	N		P	A	T	H	O	S
H	E	C	T	I	C		U	
	A		S	H	O	T	S	
V	E	R	D	I		R		H
	J	A	U	N	D	I	C	E
S	E	W	N		R	O	L	E
	C	A	C	H	A	L	O	T
S	T	Y	E		B	E	G	S

122

123

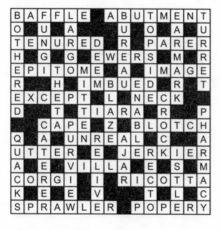

124

6	1	4	3	8	2	5	7	9
5	9	2	6	1	7	8	3	4
7	8	3	5	9	4	2	6	1
8	3	1	7	4	5	9	2	6
2	6	7	1	3	9	4	8	5
9	4	5	8	2	6	3	1	7
4	2	6	9	7	8	1	5	3
3	7	8	4	5	1	6	9	2
1	5	9	2	6	3	7	4	8

125

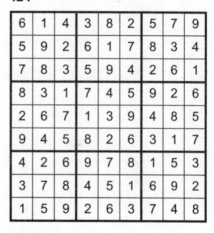

126

B	E	N	E	F	I	T
M	A	X	I	M	U	M
W	E	L	F	A	R	E
G	R	E	A	T	E	R
A	T	T	U	N	E	D
C	O	M	P	A	C	T
S	O	M	E	O	N	E

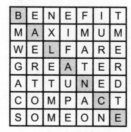

Solutions

127

128

129

5	2	7	6	1	4	3
6	7	3	4	5	2	1
1	6	2	5	3	7	4
4	1	5	3	2	6	7
3	4	1	2	7	5	6
7	5	6	1	4	3	2
2	3	4	7	6	1	5

130

8	5	9	6	7	4	2	1	3
1	7	3	2	8	9	4	6	5
6	4	2	1	5	3	9	7	8
9	8	5	3	2	6	1	4	7
2	6	1	7	4	8	3	5	9
7	3	4	9	1	5	6	8	2
3	9	7	8	6	1	5	2	4
4	2	6	5	3	7	8	9	1
5	1	8	4	9	2	7	3	6

131

3	3	1	4	6	0	1
4	2	2	3	4	3	1
0	0	6	5	6	2	3
1	0	4	4	6	4	0
0	4	2	6	1	6	4
2	2	6	3	3	0	5
5	1	2	0	5	2	5
3	1	6	5	5	1	5

132

Solutions

133

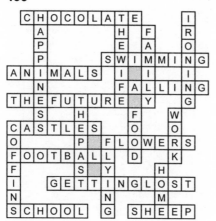

134

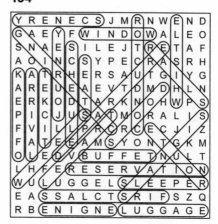

135

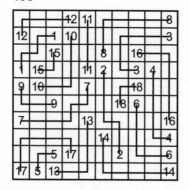

136

137

The nine-letter word is:
OBSERVING

138

	H		V			B		M
L	E	G	I	S	L	A	T	E
	A		E			R		A
C	R	O	W	S	N	E	S	T
	T	A	S	T	E		P	
		F		E	X	T	R	A
G	E	S	T	A	T	I	O	N
	A		D		E	G	O	
S	T	U	F	F	E	D		I
	U	R	E	A		O	W	N
A	P	S	E	S		W	E	T
		A	T	T	E	N	D	S

139

8	6	7	2	9	1	3	4	5
3	1	4	5	8	7	9	2	6
9	2	5	6	4	3	7	8	1
1	9	2	8	3	5	4	6	7
4	3	8	7	6	9	1	5	2
5	7	6	4	1	2	8	9	3
6	5	9	3	7	4	2	1	8
7	8	1	9	2	6	5	3	4
2	4	3	1	5	8	6	7	9

Solutions

140

N	S		I	M	P	E	R	M	E	A	B	L	E
E	A	T	E	N		L		O		I		I	
C		E		S	H	A	M	E	L	E	S	S	L	Y
K	H	A	K	I		Z		L		L		A	
E		M		G		A	C	Q	U	I	E	S	C	E
R		R	E	N	T		H		S		H		X
C	O	O		I		E		K		S	O	F	A
H		L		A	T	H	E	I	S	T		W		G
I	S	L	E		I		T		R		J	U	G
E		E		T		A		M	E	N	U		E
F	O	R	T	N	I	G	H	T		A		M		R
	V		U		V		R		S	E	P	I	A
P	O	R	T	M	A	N	T	E	A	U		I		T
	L		O		T		E		R	A	N	G	E
C	O	U	R	T	E	O	U	S	L	Y		G		D

141

C	S	A	T	O	E	R	T	E	R	C	C	A	R	D
U	K	U	S	T	I	E	S	L	H	D	A	I	S	T
B	C	P	W	C	S	M	R	A	O	R	R	L	E	I
E	A	R	L	E	I	M	O	X	U	E	E	E	L	P
U	R	O	R	A	I	T	W	S	D	S	V	C	A	R
Z	T	P	O	I	M	D	C	Y	E	R	S	B	U	A
H	C	E	S	J	G	A	E	D	K	O	E	A	E	T
X	U	R	T	S	T	G	R	E	A	G	R	N	S	S
G	T	T	R	T	Y	P	I	D	I	N	D	A	H	E
U	O	I	U	R	R	J	D	N	D	I	C	H	E	H
X	U	E	M	O	N	E	N	V	G	N	M	M	E	C
G	T	S	H	B	O	E	E	S	D	N	O	Y	T	R
P	A	C	K	E	R	E	W	E	N	U	R	T	A	O
I	N	S	R	S	B	A	C	K	D	R	O	P	E	P
A	H	B	L	A	C	K	O	U	T	D	Y	E	R	S

142

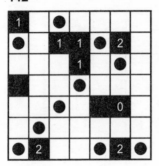

143

Answer: HUMANITY

144

1	2	3	5	6	4
5	6	1	3	4	2
3	1	4	2	5	6
2	4	6	1	3	5
6	3	5	4	2	1
4	5	2	6	1	3

145

3	5	9	2	4	6	1	8	7
1	2	4	7	3	8	5	6	9
6	8	7	9	1	5	4	2	3
9	3	8	1	5	7	6	4	2
2	1	5	4	6	9	7	3	8
4	7	6	3	8	2	9	1	5
8	4	2	5	9	1	3	7	6
5	6	1	8	7	3	2	9	4
7	9	3	6	2	4	8	5	1

Solutions

146

```
  D   G   I   U
R A T I O N A L
  E R R   C I T Y
  D O L L A R   E
S A T   O   I R A
  L   O O D L E S
B U R S T   Y E T
  S   M   R   D
    D O Z E N   H
L A O S   M O T E
  L O I N   O A R
G E M S   A N T E
```

147

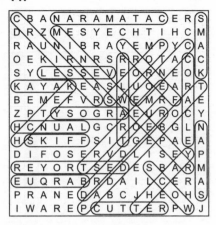

148

```
L A V A   B U N C H   A F A R
U     L E A   Y   U     L   E
T A X I   T O M A T O   A   A
E   B   C   P   V O W E L
    S I G H   H A Z E     Y
R U T   U   R   R   N A K E D
I   U   S H E A T H   A   U
D E P O T   T   E   C U R E S
E   O   Q U A R T O   A   K
S T R I P   R   Y   L   T R Y
  W   L E N S   J A P E
C O Y P U   U   E   A     R
L   A   S T I G M A   S O F A
A   W   I   A   N E T     Y
M E N U   C U R B S   A X I S
```

149

O	X	O	O	X	O	X	X
O	O	X	X	O	X	O	X
X	O	O	X	O	X	X	O
O	X	O	X	O	X	O	X
X	O	O	X	O	X	O	X
O	X	X	O	X	O	X	O
X	X	O	X	O	X	O	O
X	O	X	O	X	O	O	X

150

```
K A S K A S K I A   B       P
E       N         L   H   U
N O A T A K   G I L A   H   E
T       H         C E D A R
U   S   U   M I L K   S   C
C H A R L E S       S   O
K   C   U   C H O P T A N K
Y   R     A   T   O     L
  F A R M I N G T O N   A
    M     T   E   E     M
    E     I   R     M   A
P E N O B S C O T   A   T
    T         A L A P A H A
  K O O T E N A I     L
            L   P E A R L
```

151

F

Solutions

152

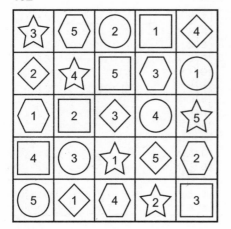

153

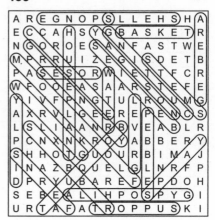

154

	W			A			A	
C	A	D	U	C	E	U	S	
	K	E	P	T		R	I	B
	E	A	T	S		G	A	R
U	N	D	O			E		A
		S		B	A	S	E	D
	N	E	W	E	L		M	
V	I	A		S	E	T	U	P
	E			I	C	E		I
	C	E	R	E		P	E	N
E	E	N		G	L	I	D	E
		D	U	E		D	O	S

155

4	6	7	8	3	2	5	1	9
9	8	1	4	7	5	2	3	6
3	2	5	1	9	6	7	4	8
2	3	6	5	8	7	4	9	1
5	7	4	9	6	1	3	8	2
1	9	8	2	4	3	6	5	7
7	1	2	3	5	8	9	6	4
8	4	3	6	2	9	1	7	5
6	5	9	7	1	4	8	2	3

156

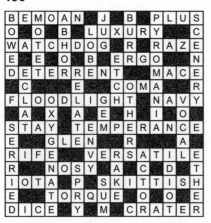

157

158

MILD - mile - mole - more - sore -
sort - SOFT
(Other solutions are possible)

Solutions

159

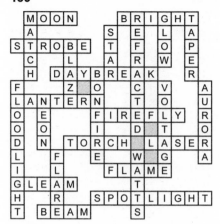

160

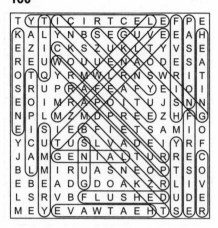

161

162

A	B	F	C	D	E
D	F	A	B	E	C
E	C	D	F	B	A
F	D	E	A	C	B
C	A	B	E	F	D
B	E	C	D	A	F

163

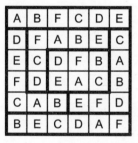

164

8	4	7	6	5	2	3	1	9
5	1	9	8	3	4	2	7	6
6	3	2	1	9	7	8	4	5
9	2	1	7	8	5	6	3	4
3	8	6	4	2	1	5	9	7
4	7	5	3	6	9	1	8	2
1	9	8	5	4	6	7	2	3
2	6	3	9	7	8	4	5	1
7	5	4	2	1	3	9	6	8

Solutions

165

E	C	D	E	C	D	B	A	B	A
D	E	B	D	A	E	C	B	A	C
B	D	A	B	E	C	D	A	C	E
A	B	C	A	B	E	C	D	E	D
C	A	E	C	D	B	A	E	D	B
D	C	B	A	E	C	E	D	B	A
E	A	C	D	B	A	D	C	E	B
C	E	D	B	A	D	A	B	C	E
B	D	A	E	C	B	E	C	A	D
A	B	E	C	D	A	B	E	D	C

166

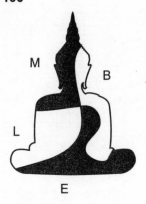

M
B
L
E

167

```
V E R S E     R O M A N     T
  P     A       O         H
B I   T     F   V         E
I C   T   C H I L D R E N S
O     R   R   C   L       I
G     E P I S T L E       S
R       M   I
A     A L L E G O R Y   F   P
P U L P     N     S A G A
H     O       C     N   R
Y     L I B R E T T O   A
      O     R   M   T   O
T R A G E D Y     I   E S S A Y
      U     A   D   Y
P O L E M I C   D Y
```

168

7